CANCER TIMES

*A beginner's guide to
prostate cancer*

MAGNUS IRVIN

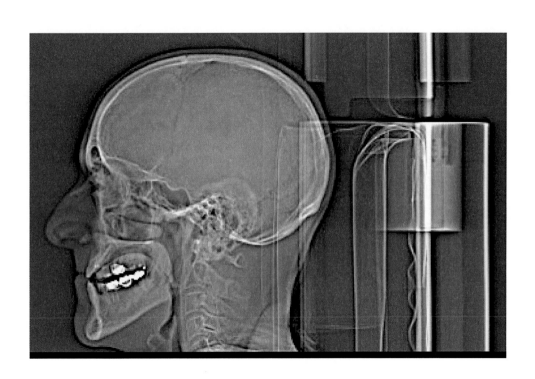

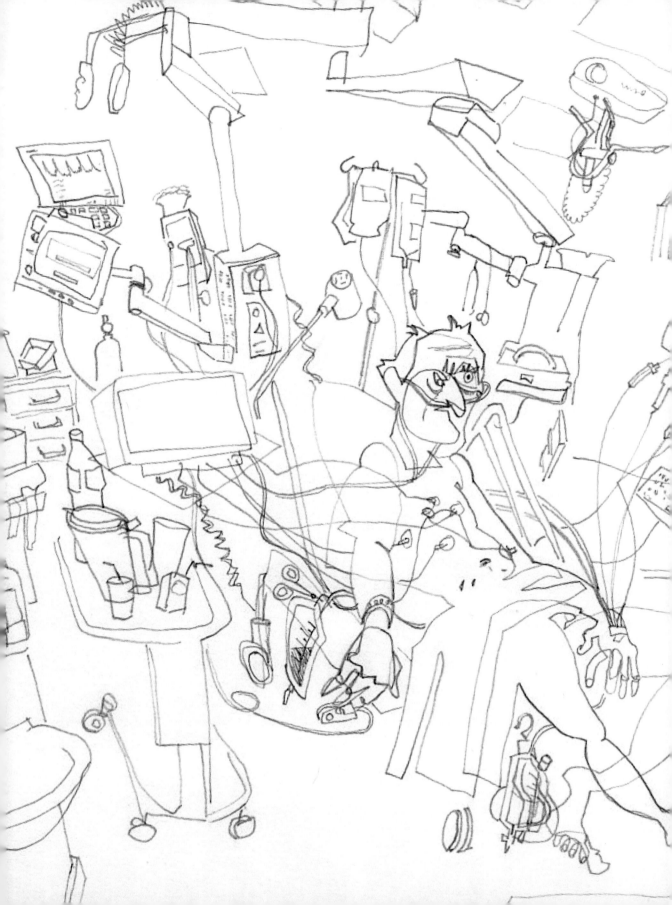

CONTENTS

FOREWORD

by Professor Heather Payne
FRCP FRCR University College London Hospitals

There are over 40,000 new diagnoses of prostate cancer every year in the UK and over 11,000 men tragically die because of the disease. This makes prostate cancer the second-most common cause of cancer-related death for men in the UK.

Prostate cancer can present in a variety of ways with disease ranging from indolent, slow-growing low-risk tumours to aggressive tumours with a high risk of progressing. There have been many advances in the last decade both in surgery and radiotherapy for localised disease, and also new drugs which allow new opportunities and hope for men with more advanced prostate cancer.

Although treatment is often a necessity for prostate cancer this can lead to important side effects which can have a significant impact on the quality of life that men experience and management should always be individualised to each man with careful attention given to his unique circumstances.

I have treated prostate cancer for over 20 years and during that time have looked after thousands of men and their families. It is a great privilege to be part of their prostate cancer journey and many patients have become friends over the past two decades.

I started to read this book one evening and found that I could not put it down until I had got to the last page, even though I knew the ending! It was a humbling experience to learn about what happens after a man leaves the consultation room and I have learnt a lot. It is not often that a medical book can make you laugh out loud and also bring a tear to the eye. This book is beautifully written with honesty and humour and is an invaluable guide to the reality of making treatment decisions for localised prostate cancer and coping with the various therapies. Although it is one man's experiences I think everyone will relate to these situations and it will make men who are facing these decisions and treatments feel better informed and less alone. I will recommend this to my patients and also my colleagues as a true insight of the impact of prostate cancer for men and their families.

INTRODUCTION

When I was diagnosed with prostate cancer I realised that friends were keen to know how I was getting on and it became clear that responding to them individually was repetitive, time-consuming and inevitably depressing.

Each morning my first thoughts explored all the avenues of uncertainty, often leading to pessimistic conclusions of an early death. Not wanting to talk about it all the time I started sending occasional, illustrated, group emails giving a personalised account of my current state of health and experiences.

Eventually I saved these messages online as an extension of my own website under the heading of Cancer Weekly. It is these written pieces that form the basis of this book. The texts, now presented under the banner of Cancer Times, have been changed very little as they were written at the actual time that I was experiencing treatments and describe how I felt then. For this reason the Cancer Times writings occasionally overlap with the factual text that explains the main aspects of my prostate cancer experience and subsequent surgery and treatments. This additional information supports the Cancer Times material and has been corroborated by the doctors and health professionals involved.

When I first told friends and family about my diagnosis I found it was difficult for them to respond and I was aware that it made some of them uncomfortable or even embarrassed. Men are notoriously bad at dealing with illness and emotional problems and I understand that people are at a loss as to how they can help. Buying gifts or offering support to a man with prostate cancer is not easy.

It is with this in mind that I have written Cancer Times in the hope that it can help de-mystify the alien world of hospitals, doctors and treatments and encourage other men and their families who will be going through the same frightening and sometimes absurd process.

The Beginning

In May 2012 I was diagnosed with locally advanced prostate cancer at the Whittington Hospital, north London. My PSA reading was 68 and my stage was T3. A biopsy revealed that the prostate contained a malignant tumour and I had a Gleason score of 4+3. I had a prostatectomy operation on the 7 August 2012. Almost eight years after diagnosis I received a 33 day course of radiotherapy to the prostate bed area.

Explanation

Locally advanced prostate cancer is cancer that has started to break out of the prostate or has spread to the area around it. The PSA test measures the amount of prostate-specific antigen in the blood. This is produced by the cancer cells and can give an indication of the stage of cancer. The average for a 60-year-old man without cancer should be about 3ng/ml (nanograms per millilitre). This test is combined with a DRE (digital rectal examination) which gives the first indications of the

stage of the tumour. Staging is measured on a T scale, (T for tumour) of 1 to 4. T1 and T2 are known as localised prostate cancer. T3 and T4 are advanced and indicate that the cancer has spread beyond the gland into the surrounding tissue.

The Gleason score looks at the pattern of cancer cells within the prostate by examining the biopsy samples. The lower the score, the lower the grade of cancer.

7 (made up of the 4+3) is a moderate score between those of slow-growing cancers and more quickly growing tumours. The Gleason score is not directly linked to the stage as there are independent risk factors. As such, it is not possible to say for certain that a Gleason score of 7 is linked to locally advanced disease. The transrectal needle biopsy involves an ultrasound scanner guiding a plastic tube that is pushed up the rectum. A needle is then passed through the wall of the rectum into the prostate where it snips out tissue samples.

The Prostate Gland

What is it?   It is a small gland found only in men

Where is it?

It's here

How big is it?

About the size of a walnut
(My one weighed 53 gms.)

What does it do?

It produces semen that mixes with sperm produced in the testicles. It also produces a protein called prostate-specific antigen (PSA) that turns the semen into liquid.

Why is it susceptible to cancer?

The causes of prostate cancer are still unknown although some factors are known to increase a man's risk.

AGE - It is estimated that around 80% of men in their 80s will have prostate cancer

ETHNIC GROUP - Black African and Caribbean men are more likely to develop prostate cancer than white men. Asian men have a lower risk of developing it.

DIET - It is thought that a diet high in animal fat (inc. dairy) and low in fruit and vegetables may increase the risk.

FAMILY HISTORY - Men with a close relative who has prostate cancer are slightly more likely to develop it themselves.

CHAPTER I
Diagnosis and Pre-operation

At the beginning of 2012 things were going well. I was getting on fine and life was good. I had a place to live, a studio and most things I needed to get by. My son had left home and was travelling the world as a diving instructor, I had a wonderful girlfriend and a job that left me plenty of time to follow my own interests. The way I saw it, I had 20 good years in front of me to continue life as an artist and traveller before I slowed down into fishing and brown pub retirement.

On 25 April of that year I visited my GP surgery complaining of pain in my lower back that had been

bothering me for a long while. I had injured it many years ago working as a scenic artist on some particularly heavy floor cloths. At the surgery I didn't see my usual doctor but a young Asian doctor standing in as a locum. She suggested I visit the Whittington Hospital for a blood test. Thinking this was a bit over the top I cycled straight there, gave a blood sample and forgot about it. A week later I received a phone call from the same doctor who told me that the tests revealed a PSA level of 68 and I had to go back to the hospital. I knew this was bad news but she explained that there were numerous reasons for a high PSA other than cancer and that I shouldn't worry – so I didn't.

On the morning of 3 May, in the company of dozens of other men, I was sitting in a rather sombre, neon-lit, corridor in the cancer department of Whittington Hospital. An hour later, after having read most of the available leaflets, I was invited into a small room where I met a tall, smartly dressed doctor who, after a few regulation questions, took off his jacket, rolled up his sleeves and snapped on a rubber glove. After I had dropped my trousers and braced myself on the back of a chair by the window he proceeded to give me a digital rectal examination as I admired the view of Highgate. This was certainly a surprise as I thought I was just coming in for a chat. After re-seating himself at his desk he told me I had an enlarged prostate gland and that I almost certainly had cancer. On hearing that I had also recently been suffering from pain in my left hip he helpfully explained that prostate cancer often migrates to the bones in this area. Finally he gave me a form to book an appointment for a prostate biopsy.

Following this experience I was sent back out into the crowded corridor to wait by a different door. As I sat there looking at the variety of men around me I thought about how very matter-of-fact, impersonal and business-like the whole procedure had been. I was thoroughly stunned and slightly outraged at the apparent lack of concern shown for my predicament. However, looking round it was clear that I was not the only one suffering.

Half an hour later I was invited into a room where I had a long talk with the specialist cancer nurse assigned to my case. I remember her well as she was the first person who offered any consolation and understanding. Noticing that I was somewhat disturbed she observed that I seemed rather shocked. I was!

There followed another waiting session so I read the appointment form I had been given and made a note of the only information on it, a scribbled T3 which I later looked up on the internet — then I knew I really had something to worry about.

It is hard to remember that period properly now as I was in a state of disorientation for several days and had decided not to tell anyone until I was really sure of my situation. A close friend who met me on the street said I was unrecognisable until he got up close. He thought I was an old man shuffling along with his shopping. Within a few days everything had changed, it was a horrible time and all my own research based on the only facts I had was deeply depressing.

The internet search for T3 cancer told me that this grade is given to a cancer that has broken through the covering layer of the prostate gland and may have metastasised to surrounding areas, usually lymph nodes, bones, bladder or bowel. Amongst other information I discovered that secondary bone cancer, although not incurable, is very bad news. A little knowledge can be a disturbing thing.

I think this was the hardest time for me with emotions running very high. On one occasion whilst having a cup of tea on the settee and considering the future Louise and I suddenly burst into tears and cried for 5 minutes.

We were both frightened.

Days passed slowly as I waited for the biopsy investigation. Having also researched this procedure, it was a hospital appointment I was not looking forward to. May 15 was a busy day for me. I arrived alone at the Whittington Hospital and went to the imaging department for an MRI scan then straight on to the biopsy department. This wing of the hospital is more modern than the old building and I sat in a much brighter, happier queue outside the biopsy room. As usual I was accompanied by a mixed bag of men of all ages, many of Afro-Caribbean origin,* all waiting for the same unwelcome treatment. Just after the patient before me had left the biopsy room a highly agitated doctor came rushing out into the corridor, introduced himself and told me to wait where I was. "I'll be back in half an hour," he said. So I decided to take a walk.

Ten minutes later the same doctor came sprinting along the corridor, sweating heavily, grabbed me and took me with him straight to the biopsy room. In no time at all my trousers were round my ankles again, my knees under my chin and something a bit too big for comfort was shoved up my backside. The sensation was not helped by the lack of lubricant. I noticed it had almost run out with the last few blobs making a bubbling noise as he tried to strangle them from the tube – not a sight which filled me with confidence. Following this uncomfortable procedure a nurse stood me back up as he ran out of the room. She explained to me that he was also on call in theatre. It was certainly dramatic.

* One in four black men will get prostate cancer in their lifetime, a high incidence that is possibly genetically linked. (Prostate Cancer UK)

Authorised

Indication - clinical right side T3. PSA 68.

Technique - large and small field of view imaging of the pelvis performed according to unenhanced prostate staging protocol.

There is a confluent area of the T2 signal measuring 2 cm x 1.5 cm in diameter within the right peripheral gland, extending towards the apex. There is associated restricted diffusion with respect to the low signal right peripheral gland focus. There is a focal bulge within the right prostatic capsule, with no definite capsular breech. The abnormal low signal crosses towards the left peripheral gland. The seminal vesicles appear atrophic.
No lateral pelvic sidewall lymphadenopathy. No retroperitoneal lymphadenopathy. No hydronephrosis.

Impression - findings consistent with confluent focus of tumour within the right peripheral gland, extending to the capsule, with focal bulging of the capsule - there is a risk of early T3a disease. The right gland requires targeting with respect to any subsequent biopsy. No associated lymphadenopathy. No bone scan performed.

Technetium 99m HDP isotope bone scan.   **Authorised**

Indication: PSA 68. Left hip pain.

Technique: Whole body images supplemented with lumbosacral SPECT.

SPECT lumbosacral spine and pelvis:

Comparison is made to the MRI study of 15 May 2012.

Focal peri-articular activity around the right L4/5 facet joint consistent with arthropathy demonstrated on previous CT of 2008. Remainder of tracer distribution in the lumbar spine is within normal limits.
There is no focal tracer activity around the left hip.
Small focal area of tracer uptake within the right iliac wing corresponds to a focal area of reduced marrow signal on MRI. A plain film in 2006 also demonstrates a benign looking lesion that is projected over the iliac bone in this region.
Focal tracer activity adjacent to the superior aspect of the left SIJ corresponds to an osseous spur that projects from the

joint margin and is most likely due to ossification of the ventral joint ligaments..

Whole body scan:
Whole body scan also demonstrates two sites of focal tracer activity within the right eighth rib posteriorly and within the left seventh rib anterolaterally. A small sclerotic lesion is present in the left seventh rib anteriorly on the CT study of 2008.
Appearances are not typical for a metastatic deposit at this time.
There is peri-articular uptake around the right ankle most likely due to arthropathy and/or previous trauma.
Some focal uptake in the right superior orbital ridge corresponds to a densely calcified benign lesion identified on CT of 4 April 2011 (?osteoma).

Opinion:
Although there are multiple sites of tracer uptake within the pelvis and thoracic cage the correlative imaging is not suspicious for metastatic disease. Suggest contemporary assessment with CT chest, abdomen and pelvis with reference to previous imaging and subsequent MDT discussion.

On 21 May I had a bone scan and 2 days later returned to the Whittington Hospital where I met Mr. Nathan, the consultant surgeon who would eventually operate to remove my prostate gland. For the first time I was able to talk to someone who had the answers to all my questions, and there were plenty of them.

The biopsy results revealed that I had a malignant tumour with a Gleason score of 4+3. I was immediately prescribed an anti-androgen drug called bicalutamide. He explained that there were now 3 courses to be considered. I could remain on hormonal drugs and expect to live a fairly normal life for maybe 5-10 years, I could have an operation to remove the prostate gland followed by radiotherapy and hopefully live a normal life-span or I could do nothing and be dead within a few years. The choice seemed obvious to me but all the same I was left with time to think about it. This was the first occasion on which I had to make an important decision myself. On the positive side, to my huge relief, the bone scan showed no signs of having spread to the pelvis although it did show signs of several old injuries.

The next choice I faced was which hospital I should continue to visit for treatment as Mr. Nathan worked at both the Whittington Hospital and UCLH (University College London

Hospitals). Before my following appointment I had done a fair amount of research and made a decision to attend UCLH in future. This was based mainly on their record in treating prostate cancer and the advanced level of equipment and facilities as well as a more modern and conducive hospital environment – something I was to value greatly. I told Mr. Nathan that I had chosen the prostatectomy operation at UCLH.

He seemed to approve and told me that he was a top international surgeon in the use of laparoscopic robotically assisted surgery and that he could operate on me using the da Vinci machine. I was impressed. I imagined a huge, eccentric machine controlled by the confident doctor sitting before me. For some reason the thought of it delicately probing around my interior was not a worrying prospect. So having made the decision my medical record was passed electronically to UCLH.

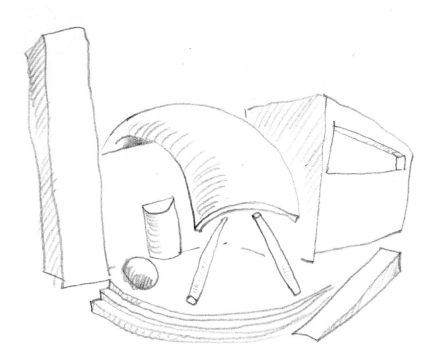

University college of London hospital – Artist's impression

There was clearly a long way to go but at least a direction was becoming apparent and to a certain extent I was coming to terms with the situation. I had conjured up an army of friends and relatives both dead and alive that I imagined were supporting me and although my son Finbarr was working far away I always pictured him with me whenever I went in to see the doctors.

It was as if his aura was protecting me from afar. I found this sort of belief and imagined assistance really helpful. Often I remembered a lost friend and invited them to join the ranks of my support army which grew by the day.

Then that I made a lucky discovery. It turned out that my friend Viki who I knew to be an anaesthetist not only worked at UCLH but also worked with Mr. Nathan. She assured me that I was in good hands and that he was a brilliant surgeon. These small things meant so much at the time.

Following an initial flurry of activity things now began to move slowly. After 2 weeks I had heard from neither hospital and there were no further appointments booked. Phone calls to both the Whittington and UCLH didn't get me far as I no longer appeared to be registered with either. Not having sufficient information I was unsure who to phone or to whom I should direct my enquiries, and ended up chasing my own tail. Meanwhile I continued to swallow the bicalutamide tablets which made me tired and a bit

The Macmillan centre UCLH

irritable. Eventually I found out that my case notes had gone astray between the two hospitals and I was lost in the system. With a little help from my friend on the inside I was eventually resurrected and was given an appointment at the UCLH Macmillan Centre which is situated a couple of streets behind the main hospital.

Two weeks later Louise and I turned up to find a brand-new building, substantially different from the dull environments I was used to. It was a sunny morning and on entering we found ourselves in an enormous, modern atrium bathed in light. In front of me in the centre of the space was a circular control desk like something out of Star Trek above which was suspended an artwork made from colourful

detritus scavenged from British beaches.

The centre has comfortable seats, tables, a cafe and a shop on the ground floor which is also the primary reception area. We were welcomed by a Macmillan volunteer who helped explain the checking-in procedure. Many of these helpers have been affected by cancer themselves and their assistance really made a big difference to our first visit.

We sat in the large reception area waiting for my name to appear on one of the many screens before going up to a smaller waiting-room on the first floor to join other patients waiting patiently (that's why we are called patients). It always interests me to see how many patients are accompanied by their family. Whilst waiting I try to guess which one of them has cancer and have sometimes been shocked to find it to be the youngest of the group.

There is so much about the hospital experience that is hard to understand for an outsider. The institutional interiors populated by staff who sometimes are not properly introduced can make for an alienating and sometimes depressing experience. Anything that can be done to help break down this impression is obviously worthwhile and the architecture of the Macmillan Centre is a huge step in the right direction. A lot of thought has been given to creating an environment, that although spacious, is built on a human scale helping visitors to feel more comfortable and confident. On all of my numerous visits I have never seen it overcrowded or suffering from the oppressive congestion that I had so often encountered previously. For those who want to explore there is a lift that will take you up to the roof garden which even on sunny days I have found empty. When I first visited the centre it was so new that the internal communications system was not working properly and it was quicker for doctors to walk

down the corridor to pass on messages to colleagues. Discovering the Macmillan Centre was a delight and I still feel that today.

My first appointment there on the morning of 4 July was with Professor Payne, consultant in clinical oncology at UCLH. She explained the treatment options available for locally advanced prostate cancer with particular reference to radiotherapy. I left feeling that the whole process had been somewhat de-mystified and I also had a clearer picture of the possible side effects involved. All additional information I was receiving went into a mental memory bank but having listened to the pros and cons of each option I was still confused as to what decision was right for me.

Two days later I met Professor Kelly, a specialist prostate cancer surgeon and head of the urology department, who I knew would be an influential factor in the progress of my treatment. I also met the Lead Clinical Nurse who would be my personal contact with the hospital and doctors.

At this meeting it was explained that although the surgery option may seem the best choice, quality of life should be taken into account. One of the main factors being that when the prostate is removed in

1560 – Leonardo designs the first Da Vinci machine

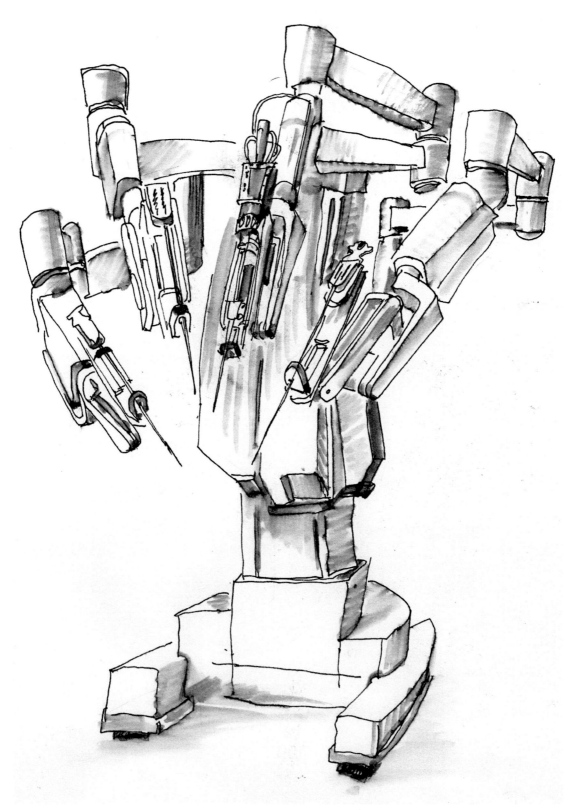

Da Vinci's latest version

a non nerve-sparing operation the ability to achieve a spontaneous erection is lost. There is also the possibility of incontinence. Professor Kelly tells me that although nothing definite is showing on my scans, based on my PSA reading of 68 the cancer will definitely have spread from the prostate.

The cancer will definitely have spread from the prostate.

This opinion was different from that of the surgeon I had already seen who said it was still contained within the prostate. It was arranged that in addition to the MRI scan I had at the Whittington, I should have a range of other tests including an ultrasound scan and also a visit to the Nuclear Medicine department for choline PET and CT scans. I was informed that I would not be offered the operation if it was considered that I had less than 10 years to live and I had the impression that could be the case.

Of course, at that time I had no idea of my possible longevity but had I been told that I did indeed have 10 years or more to live I think I would have been fairly happy as most of the information gleaned from my previous hospital meetings had put me in fear of an early death.

Scans are easy if you are not claustrophobic and don't mind lying still for a while, but it was the results that were worrying me. The MRI scanner is a large machine that makes a lot of noise. The patient lies on a bed that slides in and out of the tubular scanner which looks like a giant ring doughnut. Once inside, there is very little space and I found my nose just inches away from the upper surface of the tube. When it starts, the magnetic device within the doughnut begins to revolve and a rhythmic noise builds up into what sounded to me like a demented drum solo. It is not exactly a relaxing racket but I did mange to fall asleep during the scan.

For those who are claustrophobic there is an alarm button should you wish to escape.

Less than 10 years!

At this time it was unknown whether my cancer had passed from the prostate into the surrounding soft tissue. Whilst waiting for the scan results we decided to have a break with a trip to the south coast in my camper van. The weather was pretty dreadful which didn't help spirits but it was good to be occupied with something different. After a couple of days, whilst unloading our bags into a small hotel, I got a phone call telling me that as far as the consultant could make out from the scans the cancer had not spread to the nearby lymph nodes and that I could relax. He also said I should not go swimming with sharks.*

A huge weight was suddenly lifted from my shoulders, and unable to control our emotions, Louise and I stood in the middle of the high street in the evening darkness and hugged each other in relief. It was great to share that moment. But there was also someone else I wanted to share it with.

Up to this point, although he knew I had cancer, I had been too worried to tell my son about how serious it was looking. He was working in Zanzibar and I decided this was

My T reading was 3, signifying that the cancer had spread outside of the capsule, the N reading was N0 meaning the cancer had not been found in the lymph nodes and my M reading was M0, meaning that the cancer had not metastasised to other parts of the body. I did not like the T reading much.

*At the previous meeting I had told the consultant that I was a scuba diver and would rather take my chances swimming with sharks.

the right time to give him the full story. The following morning we had a long phone conversation, me sitting on a bench in the rain in the grounds of Arundel Castle and him on an island in the Indian Ocean. I felt a lot better after that.

Things were beginning to look up but as usual any feeling of elation was short lived. The abdominal scans did not pick up signs of cancer in surrounding tissue or bones although those of the prostate itself showed an internal growth that was fighting to break through the outer layer of the gland. The stage that prostate cancer has reached is gauged by the TNM system.

INCIDENCE

- There were over 47,000 new cases of prostate cancer in the U.K. in 2015. That's 129 cases diagnosed every day.
- 9 out of 10 prostate cancer cases are diagnosed in men aged 60 or over.
- 1 in 8 men will be diagnosed with prostate cancer in their lifetime.
- It is estimated that by 2030 prostate cancer will be the most commonly diagnosed cancer in the U.K.
- Prostate cancer accounts for 1 in 4 (26%) male cancer cases in the U.K.
- More men are now dying from prostate cancer than women are from breast cancer (2018)

Statistics from Prostate Cancer UK 2018

CANCER TIMES

Monday 2nd July 2012 | magnusirvin.com/cancerweekly | **No 1**

CAPT. MAGNO ONE IN 47,300
A popular choice for men

DA VINCI STEPS IN!

The Choice

It's Make Your Mind Up Time.

Magnus Irvin

Dear friends and readers, welcome to Cancer Times, an occasional report on my prostate cancer experience.

Sorry about the impersonal email

but time may be short. Just a quick word to bring you up to date with my dodgy situation.

The bad news is I still have cancer but the good news is that the da Vinci machine is going to operate on me some time in the

next 5 weeks or so. I was given the choice between 2 treatments without the doctors advising any preference. After deciding on having the operation they all looked quite happy and said it was a good choice.

Nice to get something right!

I also had some say regarding the surgeon who will control the robot and found I could have a doctor with shaky hands do it in 2 weeks or the renowned Mr. Nathan, who doesn't appear to have the DTs, do it when he gets back from holiday. Thereafter I'll have a month sitting on my sore bum before 7 weeks of radiotherapy. Can't wait.

It appears that there are over 200 types of cancer each with their own complex treatments. With the prostate option I have at last become mainstream and chosen quite a popular one. One may even say trendy.* However, I'm not sure that the summer is a good time to get the diagnosis. The positives are that given my change of diet, all fruit and veg are abundant and

the unpredictable British weather suits my moods perfectly. Amongst the numerous negatives is that all the doctors, surgeons and consultants are on holiday trying to forget about me stuck here with the lurgy.

The radiotherapist appears to be the most positive doctor I've met so far telling me that, with a bit of luck, it is possible this "bloody nuisance" can be eradicated. A nice change from the doctors who

have a neat way of feeding you more and more depressing info on each hospital visit.

That's about it really apart from thanking so many of you who've offered help, advice and support. I'm overwhelmed and grateful. Keep up the good work, it's excellent medicine.

All's well in Casa Magno today. I hope it is wherever you are.

Worried but OK.

.

Of course, it's not a trend that I can claim to have started. There are many previous trail-blazers including Nelson Mandela, Roger Moore, Harry Belafonte, Frank Zappa, Robert de Niro, Stormin' Norman Schwarzkopf, Bernard Moitessier, Timothy Leary, Billy Connolly, Bob Monkhouse, Johnny Ramone, Kojak and Uggi the dog from the film "The Artist". I see even Ben Stiller has jumped on the bandwagon.

PROSTATE CANCER STAGES

T2b

Tumour involves more than one half lobe, but not both lobes, remains within prostate capsule.

TX, T0, T1, T1a, T1b, T1c

Tumour can not be felt.

T2, T2a

Tumour can be felt, but is confined to one half of the lobe or less, and remains within the prostate capsule (the membrane that encloses the prostate gland).

T2c

Tumour involves both lobes, remains within prostate capsule.

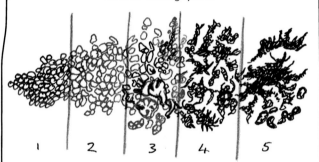

Gleason Grading System

1. Cells from the tumour look like normal prostate cells.

2. Cells look like normal prostate cells but are less tightly packed than normal.

3. Cells resemble normal prostate cells but are more seperated and have ill-defined edges which go into the tissue between the cells.

4. Cells do not look like normal prostate cells.

5. Cells look like cells from other types of tumours.

The overall Gleason score is calculated by adding the most common grade of cells in the biopsy sample with the second most common.

T3, T3a

Tumour extends through prostate capsule.

T3b

Tumour extends through prostate capsule and invades seminal vesicle(s).

T4

Tumour is fixed or invades adjacent structures other than the seminal vesicles:

bladder neck, external sphincter rectum, levator muscles or pelvic wall.

On July 6 I once again visited the excellent Macmillan Centre for an appointment with Dr. Cathcart, one of Professor Kelly's team. He told me that Mr. Nathan was convinced the cancer was contained and he could remove it all. It was decided that a laparoscopic operation should be carried out within the next 5 weeks. To help clarify matters he even drew a small diagram of my prostate before admitting he was no artist. I thought it had a rather profound, naive quality.

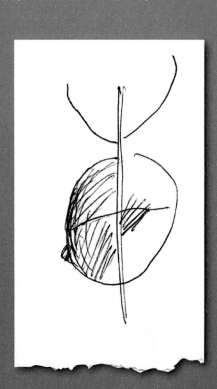

Eventually, after an SMDT discussion in which one senior consultant argued that my days were numbered, it was decided to offer me the operation. I have subsequently found out that my case was helped a lot by another consultant who argued strongly that I was a salvageable prospect.

It was then up to NICE to make a judgement and in late summer I got the news that my operation was scheduled for the 7 August 2012, the day before my dad's 86th birthday. At this point I had told most friends and some family but it still remained a secret from my elderly parents for fear that they might die of shock. At my next appointment a week later the surgeon said it was still not possible to be sure whether the cancer had already passed through the capsule and we would not know until after the operation, when samples of surrounding tissue would also be taken. Things were beginning to look up. But as usual, any feeling of elation was temporary as soon after I was told that the PET scan had detected a nodal lesion which might indicate the cancer had spread to a lymph node.

Statistics from Prostate Cancer UK 2018

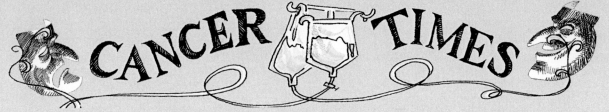

CANCER TIMES

Sunday 15th July 2012 | magnusirvin.com/cancerweekly | No 2

Are cancer and fishing luck related?

Important new research findings

Magnus Irvin

Dear Readers,

I have now taken up a new anti-cancer diet and forsaken the joys of cakes, puddings and custard in favour of everything that is green, raw and tastes rather vile.

My charming girlfriend Louise and I drove down to Arundel where we found a small hotel with a 15th century ceiling imported from a Medici palace. Lovely place but the owner was a bit miffed that we didn't eat his wonderful nosh. So was I, it all looked marvellous. He would have been even more upset if he'd seen what we were doing in our room with all that raw veg and a blender. We managed to smuggle it all into our next place in Eastbourne where we once again made a horrific mess leaving green stains on all the towels after trying to wash the used blender, plates, glasses and machete in the shower.

RADIOACTIVE LOOS:
Discover more inside

Radioactive Loo

Louise can now drive my van and has just got the hang of changing gear, now she only has to master the steering. Having driven up numerous kerbs and removed the wing mirror from a Transit van it makes for an interesting ride but perhaps not perfect for someone wanting to avoid stress.

The normal breakfast chaos ensued when she used the guest-house kitchen to liquidise a field-full of brassicas before dyeing the landlady's hair pink. Neither the use of the kitchen nor the hair colour met with approval from her family and they were glad to see us leave.

Last week I visited the nuclear medicine department at the hospital which I found to be unnervingly deserted and quiet. A nurse sat me on a recliner where I waited for the syringe which turned up in a small metal container. After an hour to let the injection circulate I had a further hour lying in the PET scanner. Whilst waiting for this I had to sit halfway down the corridor in case my presence affected the readings in the department where they were trying to stabilise the radioactivity.

Feeling the call of nature I mistakenly urinated in the wrong toilet for which I was told off by a nurse. I'd forgotten that I was radioactive and only supposed to use the toilet with the yellow and black trefoil sign on the door. I later saw someone going into the toilet with a Geiger counter and a bucket. I think André Breton would have approved.

After all this I took a break in Planet Organic where I was pleased to assume that I was the only radioactive customer.

My theory that cancer increases fishing luck is now looking more likely. A few weeks ago I caught 6 barbel in the space of 4 or 5 hours - a fine feat given that I'd never caught one previously. Then more recently a bag of several chub and roach helped to support my belief.

I'm wondering whether the time has come to start taking hard recreational drugs? Having been cautious in the past I'm now thinking that heroin could be a worthwhile experience. I've always believed that hard drugs in later life shouldn't be too problematic. Who's going to care if an 80-yr-old becomes a heroin addict and I doubt if it can be any worse than drug-addled later years with dementia in a home? May be a bit early for me yet but certainly something for the future.

Nice to get out of London for a while but all a bit fraught as I am still waiting for results of the biopsy and scans.

Hoping this finds you well

Magnus x

So how are we today Mr. Irvin?

Super Looloo's visit.

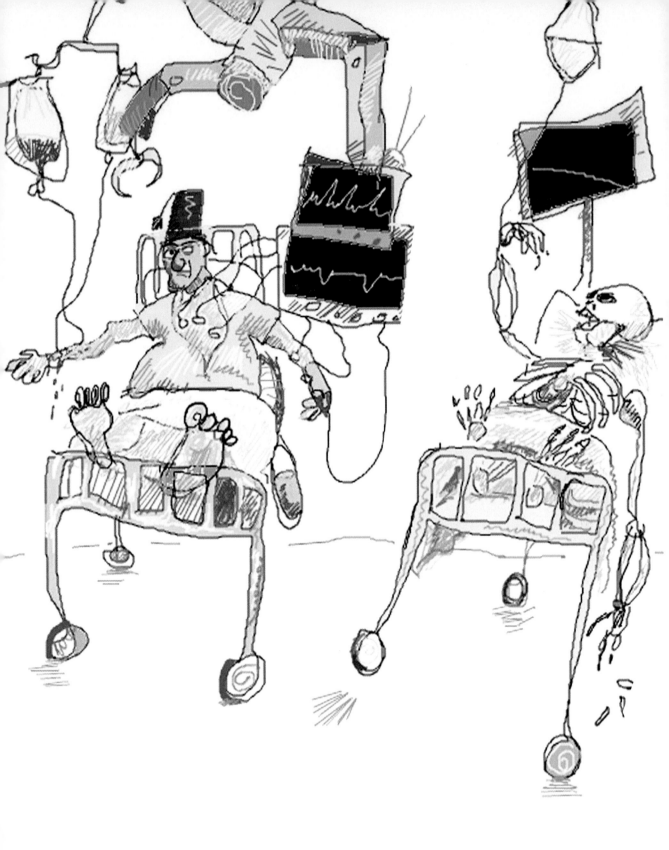

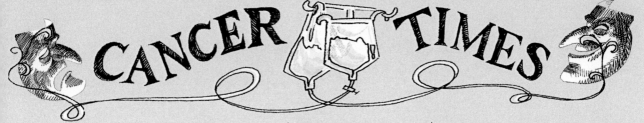

CANCER TIMES

Monday 30th July 2012 | magnusirvin.com/cancerweekly | **No 3**

R.A.L.R.P.
So What's That Mean Then?

The Da Vinci Machine

Magnus Irvin

Having just had a pre-op assessment and finding myself lighter to the tune of a few more pints of blood and wee, I am glad to be told that there's nothing wrong with me despite an 'abnormal' ECG test and I am the perfect candidate for surgery.

The good news is that the grandly titled Robotic Assisted Laparoscopic Radical Prostatectomy will take place on the 7 August. The surgeon is Mr. Nathan who has used this daVinci machine before and is supposed to be quite good at it. He will operate

it from a booth with hand controls like a games console. The photos of the robot show something looking like a mechanical octopus with 4 arms. 3 of them have cutting instruments and the other is a camera so with a bit of luck there should be a good film available soon. The surgical instruments enter via a number of portholes cut in the abdomen and the snippers and tweezers are changed by the surgical assistant whilst the surgeon tries to improve his Super Mario Brothers score on the screen. It all sounds rather wonderful but unfortunately I'm unlikely to see any of it.

The bad news is I'd just bought an air ticket to get me to the Weiterstadt film festival on the 9th and I can't get my money back.

Sorting out appointments at UCLH appears to be a hit and miss affair. I've learnt to phone the chap at reception who arranges all this in order to avoid delay. Once a date is made on the phone you later receive a letter of confirmation. These almost always turn up the day after you have attended the appointment. However, last week I got an unexpected letter telling me to come in on 10 October. Nobody appears to know what this is for but it does say something for their faith in my longevity.*

The pre-existing dizziness that has affected me for a couple of years has become worse (probably due to stress or the gender-bender drugs) so I went to the Throat, Nose and Ears hospital where I was given a few exercises including walking up and down stairs with my eyes closed. Doesn't seem to help much but perhaps they think a broken leg will take my mind off other matters. I also had a tooth removed due to fracturing a root whilst chomping on all those bloody nuts and seeds I eat. As I left the dentist my mouth was bleeding, I felt dizzy, it was pouring with rain and I reminded myself I also have cancer. Things can only get better?

One of the benefits of my condition is that I have no trouble with those horrid, happy young people that come bounding up on Mare St. hoping to sell me something or the other. When they cheerfully grin "Hey, how are you?" I reply "I've got cancer. How about you?" It's cruel but it does the trick.

Many thanks to everyone who has kept in touch and sent all sorts of edifying advice including the beneficial effects of salvestrols,

coffee enemas, apricot kernels, Slippery Elm powder, broken wall Chlorella, Horny Goatweed and of course the Mediterranean Death Carrot. Do keep it up, just the thought of them is a tonic.

After the op I'll be recuperating at Louise's place. Visitors are welcome and I will be pleased to show my new scars and demonstrate the workings of my catheter and urinary leg bag.

I hope you are well wherever you are. Next week's Cancer Times may be a bit late.

Arranging appointments can be a bit unpredictable. A couple of times I have received a last-minute phone call telling me my appointment has been cancelled and have also turned up for an appointment to be told it was cancelled weeks ago - "you should have received a letter you know". Recently I successfully attended an appointment at the Pain Management Centre only to find a text on my phone that arrived whilst I was talking to the consultant informing me that my appointment had been cancelled and not to come in. Some appointment texts are accompanied by the information that if you (me) fail to attend it costs the NHS £137.

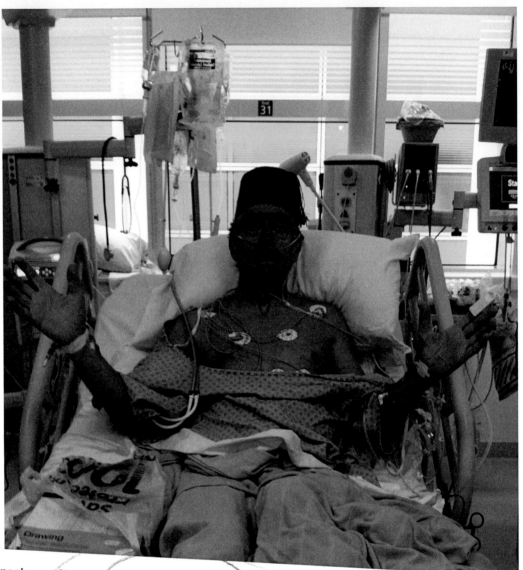

Diagnosis: Gleason 4+3 locally advanced prostate cancer
Presenting PSA 68
TRUS biopsy Gleason 4+3 12 out of 12 cores
MRI prostate T3a disease.
No evidence of metastases on bone scan
PET scan - ? solitary node.

Treatment: radical robotic prostatectomy 7.8.2012 – histology shows Gleason 4+3 pT3a
(1mm) bilateral disease, 13 obturator nodes were clear.
Close monitoring of PSA for early salvage radiation if required

Current situation: No evidence of disease recurrence

It was a pleasure to review Mr Irvin in Dr Payne's Oncology clinic today who came accompanied with his
wife. He is currently two years post-robotic radical prostatectomy.

CHAPTER 2
Operation and Aftermath

The night before my operation Louise and I went to the Olympic Park in Stratford to see athletes jumping over sticks and chucking weights around in the London Olympics. It certainly took my mind off things although I was aware that after tomorrow my life would not be the same again. I don't remember feeling particularly nervous and I slept well. In the morning Louise and I indulged in a fond farewell to my last ever spontaneous erection and as I was not allowed a breakfast she drove me to the hospital.

The day of the operation flew by. I was admitted at 7am. My friend Viki visited me. I had put all my own clothes in the shoulder bag I carried with me and replaced them with the outfit I found in a sealed plastic bag at the foot of the bed which contained anti-VTE stockings, an ill-fitting blue gown with matching paper hat and underpants. I was visited by a doctor who explained what the operation would involve, I signed the consent form and a number of other papers and had

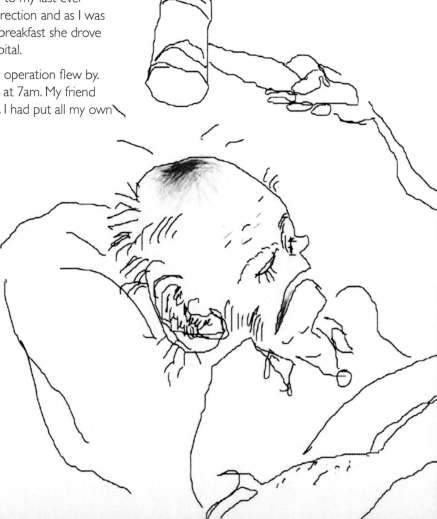

a long chat to the anaesthetist, a well-dressed chap wearing a red buttonhole in his pinstriped suit. My operation must have been the first of the day as I was soon wheeled into the theatre, a fascinating environment that I had little time to appreciate. I thought it would be a great place to do an artist's residency. I'm sure they could sit me in the corner with a pencil and paper, I wouldn't be any trouble. I remember that I wasn't worried at all and was even looking forward to the anaesthetic. The lovely feeling of it creeping up my body is the last thing I remember until later that day.

The period between the anaesthetic and waking up disappeared in the blink of an eye. I spent an unknown period drifting in and out of dreams to the sound of machines beeping and lights flashing.

I came round in the intensive care unit, the lights were low and someone was sitting on the chair next to me. There were only 4 beds in the post-anaesthesia care unit. In the bed opposite mine a man was rolling around and muttering loudly. He appeared to be secured to his bed by a great mass of wires and tubes. Had I been able to see myself I would have realised that I was similarly tied to a whole battery of machines and bags. As I slowly came round I recognised my first visitor as my friend Diamond Dave. After a while I asked him how he had been. "God, I feel terrible," was his reply, "I don't know what's wrong with me but I've felt dreadful all week". Fortunately after a hazy conversation I was able to get him back on a stable footing and send him home with a prescription for less alcohol and more sleep. It was nice to hear someone else's problems.

Later that day Louise turned up and my shoulder bag was returned to me. In it I found a fez and a packet of adhesive moustaches.

In the afternoon I was moved into a normal ward where the patients looked even worse. Even the man pushing the hoover around looked like a zombie. I was filled with painkillers and fed 3 times a day and at night I was given a pump to self-administer a most welcome painkiller. The Graseby 3300 PCA pump is a most benevolent machine containing 2 oz. of morphine which I was using very effectively until it packed up in the middle of the night. It let out a loud screech that woke everyone else in the ward and was taken away, not to be replaced. The pain in my groin persisted with a vengeance until, after exhausting all other painkillers. I was eventually prescribed something more serious that managed to take the edge off it and made me feel rather happy.

I was in hospital for only a few days before moving in to Louise's place where I spent most of my time supine on the settee. I had a few weeks here recuperating and nursing the 5 small scars where the da Vinci machine had entered my abdomen. I was visited by Bridget, a fellow artist who had enjoyed a similar operation for ovarian cancer and we compared scars. For 2 weeks I wore a djellaba and a catheter attached to a urinary leg bag. The djellaba which I had bought in Cairo many years ago suddenly became a most useful and necessary item of clothing. With the discomfort caused by surgery and the extremely inconvenient catheter and bag it was impossible to get a pair of trousers on. Besides which I looked great!

CANCER TIMES

Saturday 11th August 2012 | magnusirvin.com/cancerweekly | No 4

DA VINCI OR POLLOCK?
Speed or precision?

FASHION PAGES
Extra holes trending. Tattoos passé

Da Vinci Returns

The Jackson Pollock machine

Magnus Irvin

Apologies again for the impersonal message but the gender-bender hormone tablets have turned me into a woman and I have become short-tempered and irrational. I am even wearing a dress as trousers are now most uncomfortable.

The da Vinci machine has done its best to get rid of this cancer and I'm sitting with my feet up minus a few bits I had last week. The operation was obviously a nippy affair coming in under the scheduled 4 hours and my prostate, which is the size of a walnut, was removed through a slit above my belly button. The same operation is a lot quicker with the Jackson Pollock machine but the results tend to be less precise. Now I wait a month or so for the histology reports following biopsy of what was removed.

My stomach is shaven and dyed yellow and my penis and one

testicle are covered in a dark purple bruise. From the waist down I look like a Chinaman with a black man's nob. I was wondering before the op how many extra holes I would wake up with and it turns out to be six. Four for the instruments to go in, one for the plastic drainage tube (like a toilet overflow which was 18 inches long when they pulled it out) and one mystery hole.

There was much celebration in the ward as the assistant surgeon shared my delight in the return of my farting muscle which was noticeably absent for a couple of days. This was followed by my first solid bowel movement which was almost white and smelt of flowers. On any other occasion it could well have been ectoplasm. My son reminded me of a great line from the white chapter in Moby Dick, "It's the paleness of it that is so appalling".

I managed to get discs of my PET and CT scans which are pretty sensational. I can scroll from the top of my head down to my feet in 350 cross-section photos. I'm also hoping to get slides of the diseased prostate as I've heard they are rather beautiful, coloured images. My bruises have now matured delightfully and I hope to do some coloured self-portraits. Should you care to join me in a life class I can recommend stocking up on orange, ochre, lemon yellow, Payne's grey and several shade of aubergine

The catheter is a proper pain and has to stay there for a couple of weeks as it is also holding my urethra in place and can't be removed until the internal stuff has healed. It's not visible under

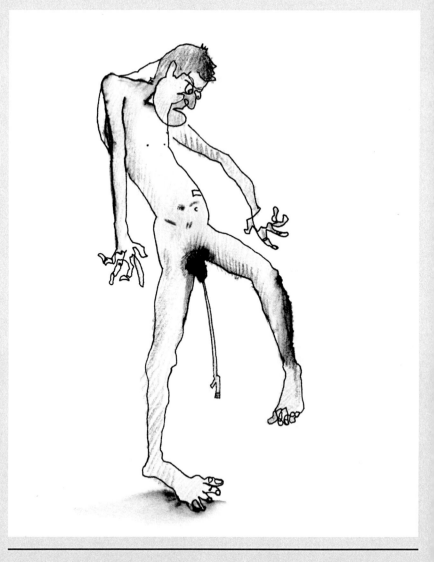

my dress but it has been suggested that if worn on the outside it may make an interesting portable leg aquarium. Perhaps a couple of Siamese fighting fish - not candiru.

I've been at Louise's for a week and it occurred to me that it may be horrible to have a bruised and scarred old man in a dress limping around her flat clutching a wee wee bag but she says it's "lovely". I wonder if this is a service that I can offer to a broader audience? Do let me know. For a small consideration I could enact scenes

from Gormenghast in your own home. Great for dinner parties.

I read that scientific studies have proved that people who are prayed for after surgery have better results than those who are not, so if it's not too much of a liberty perhaps I could ask those with faith to spare a minute or two.

There is no definite reason as to why one may contract cancer but in my case I'm pretty sure I got it from Louise's dog.

Catheters akimbo.

54

On my next visit to the surgical department I was told that everything was going well. The surrounding tissue samples including numerous lymph nodes showed no sign of further cancer. This was the best news I'd had for

"Well he would, wouldn't he. He's a surgeon."

a good while and not for the first time I found myself fighting back tears of relief. It is strange how the good news often brings such a response whereas the bad news is accepted with equanimity.

Mr. Nathan said my PSA reading had fallen to the surprisingly low level of -0.01. That evening we opened a bottle of champagne which gave me indigestion, I was

no longer match fit when it came to drinking alcohol. Once again bad news followed good. At my next appointment with a consultant in the radiotherapy department I was told that due to my initially high PSA reading and the state of my prostate, it was very likely that the cancer had moved on and that the operation probably had not completely removed it. It was suggested that I consider further treatment in the form of radiotherapy with more hormonal drugs. "But the surgeon said he's removed the cancer and I won't need radiotherapy," I told them. "Well he would, wouldn't he. He's a surgeon." was the response and it was the first time I realised that interdepartmental harmony is not always what I imagined.

So I had to decide whether or not to have radiotherapy?

This was a difficult choice with one camp saying "what's the point? You don't need it" and the other saying "it's a way of being more certain that we have mopped up all the cancer cells". The radiologists believed that cells had probably passed from the prostate into the body and could be anywhere. There was also a strong presumption that there would be cells left over around the operation site in the area of the urethra and bladder where my prostate used to be. I wonder where it is now? The prostate-bed radiotherapy would be targeted in this area. So I got all the information I could muster and eventually chose not to have it, mainly swayed by information concerning possible side effects and a belief that a strong immune system could handle stray cells.

Once again my decision was accepted without argument. It is still a matter of time before we know if it was the right one. They say it will take 10 years until a man can be certain that the cancer has gone.

I was also asked to take part in a clinical study called the Radicals Trial. This was a test to help ascertain the best time for radiotherapy to be used after surgery. If I signed up for it I would be randomly placed in one of two categories – to have radiotherapy or continue without it – the decision would not be mine. Although I really wanted to be part of this trial I had already made up my mind and I declined the offer.

My hospital routine changed to a visit every 3 months alternating between surgical and radiology teams. At these meetings I receive the PSA and testosterone results from my latest blood test and the progress of the cancer is discussed. On each occasion Louise comes with me. I now call her Lucky Loo Loo as ever since she first came along the outlook has improved. A friend who had cervical cancer warned me that on the first hospital visits the news gets worse and worse. This was certainly true for me. It seems you have to weather the storm before things begin to brighten up.

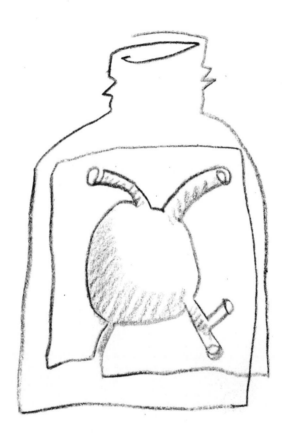

CANCER TIMES

Friday 7th September 2012 | magnusirvin.com/cancerweekly | No 5

More Wee Wee

Magnus Irvin

The good news is the catheter, which was the diameter of a drainpipe, has been removed and I no longer go everywhere with a bag of urine strapped to my leg looking like Dr. Phibes. It also means I can pass through airport security without problems regarding fluids.

After nearly 3 weeks of that attachment I now enjoy my new freedom of movement but am engaged in a fight to control incontinence. I find myself in the privileged, pot-luck situation of being able to fart with or without wetting my pants at the same time. It's all to do with the coordination between the clacker valve* and the bladder sphincter. In order to make this matter less messy whilst trying to regain control of the pelvic floor, I am armed with a box of Discreet Male Protective

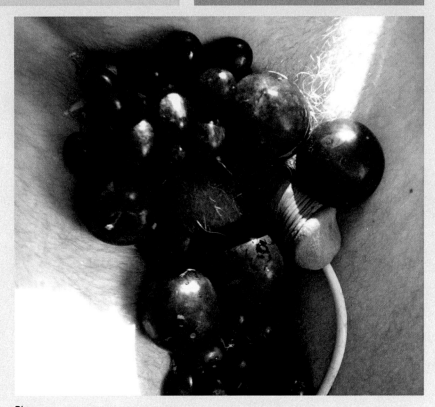

Plums

Pads (nappies) that I stick in the gusset of my newly purchased, large-size Y-fronts. On the outside of the box it says "Now with new more masculine pack design". That's good, I wouldn't want to look like a sissy.

The adhesive strip on the nappies takes a bit of getting used to. On a couple of attempts I have managed to stick it to the end of my nob causing considerable pain in removal. I wonder why the glue has to be that strong? Is it because they are made in Sweden by masochists?

Our fashion correspondent Ms. Xteen says that Gucci's marketing line for their spring 2013 collection will be "If you're rich take the piss". Assuming the urinary leg bag will not be in their collection, the Cancer Times design team have come up with a range of their own. If you know anyone with enough dosh to pay for an ad in Vogue it could be rather fun? A must for the glitterati fashionistas.

Walking down Mare St. the other day I saw a young man holding a sign made from a cereal packet saying "FREE PRAYER" (aren't they all?). He asked how I was so I told him and he put his hand on my shoulder whilst his attractive assistant held my arm and they offered a rather touching prayer asking God to bring me strength and good health. It was a strangely moving experience unhindered by any other agenda. I came away tearful and happy. As I left he told me that during my healing process God may reveal himself to me. I rather hope he does.

That evening I went to see the Pretty Things in the Eel Pie Club and as I watched those old rockers I wondered how their prostates were. Whilst there my friend Dr. Manic gave me a powerful Buddhist chant that I have to repeat - nam my-oho renge kyo!

Although returning to work is something for the future, with Louise's camera and direction we have made a number of films illustrating additional uses for the catheter and portable wee wee bag. They will not be to everyone's taste so maybe I'll put them on my Vimeo site rather than in an attachment. I hope that in future they will be seen as educational and form part of a blockbuster show of cancer

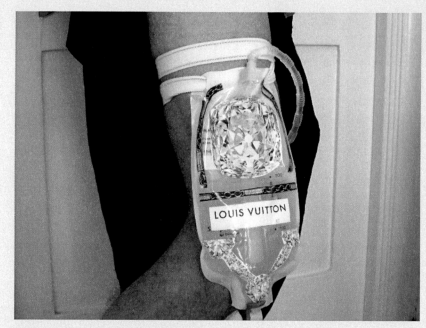

All new Louis Vuitton urinary leg bag is this years must have accessory

art and entertainment. I have also discovered that the discs of my PET and MRI scans contain some really great hidden images. With the right software these can be viewed in 3D. I'm hoping to meet the head of the imaging department at the hospital who has expressed interest in working with an artist.

The next episode in this exciting drama occurs on 14 September when I go to see the specialist team at UCLH for biopsy results, pathology report and the plan for future treatment. I have learnt through my previous experience of these meetings that a stiff upper lip is useful (not much else is stiff at the moment). However, I'm having a Macmillan reflexology session beforehand so probably by the time I get to them I'll be cured.

Once again, thanks to all who have sent their good wishes. I am aware that candles have been lit, prayers prayed, chants chanted, offerings burnt and notes hung on trees of life. Also thanks for all correspondence received, much of which has been most illuminating. Dr. Slim Lucas confirms my belief with the following – "I hear from an informed friend that your theory about contracting cancer from Louise's dog is very plausible and that this is quite common". Just as I suspected!

Also, just in case things downstairs don't fully return to normal my Australian brother in cancer Herr Heinz Krautberger has suggested I could join him in employment as a harem guard, and nurse de la Hey points out that my 6 abdominal stigmata put me 2 up on Jesus.

Nappies ahoy!

Thanks to Dr. Davis for giving me the correct term for the anal sphincter.

nam my-oho renge kyo

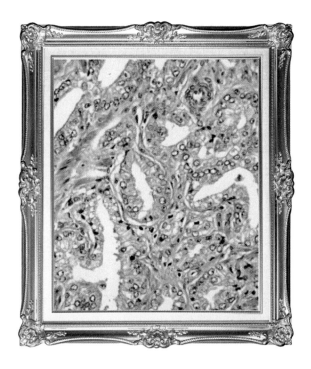

When I was first diagnosed my PSA was 68. After taking the bicalutamide it dropped to 54 and eventually to 28. After the operation it was -0.01. I had the operation over 6 years ago now and since then the PSA reading has gradually crept up and now stands at 1.12. These are small increases and the doctors say it gives them no cause for concern. However, the level has risen and nobody can say for certain whether it is cancer or not.

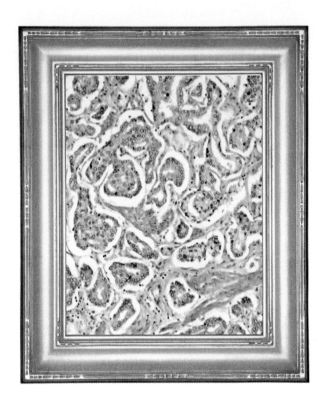

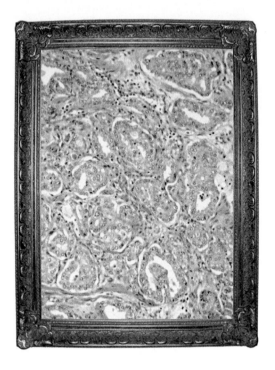

There is the possibility that some healthy prostate cells have remained after the operation and they are still producing PSA. I now only visit the radiology department and am scheduled for an annual MRI scan. A friend pointed out that I was actually the lucky one as I would know quickly if the cancer returned whereas many men can have it for years, sometimes finding out too late. Nice to be the lucky one.

Tim Hyman's drawing of me
at the Maggie's Centre in London.

CANCER TIMES

Monday 24th September 2012 | magnusirvin.com/cancerweekly | **No 6**

Alternative Remedies

EUTHANASIA
Special offers this week

Magnus Irvin

Much has happened since the last issue of this infrequent ramble and my search for cancer cures traditional, alternative and completely odd continues.

I recently visited a Maggie's Centre at Charing Cross Hospital, where my friend Tim Hyman is artist in residence, and I dropped in on a prostate group meeting at which a rather dour doctor talked about palliative care (dealing with the very sick and incurables). Not very cheerful until one of the group started talking about the Dignitas clinic in Zurich where they will end it all for you. The lecturer had a dim view of this saying that it costs £10,000 a go (only one go necessary, surely) and suggested that with good palliative care it's something we needn't be concerned about. I wondered if she could do it cheaper? This led to talk about what qualifications are needed to set up one's own murder clinic. After that it was a lot more fun. It didn't really seem an appropriate subject for a group of men all

Wrabness mud therapy

was not available 7 years ago they wouldn't have wasted that sort of operation on me if they thought I was going to peg it soon. They could do with him back at the hospital.

The cancer fishing luck seems to be holding out with a recent catch of 2 tench and a big roach that was seized on the way in by a monster pike which snapped my line. Cancer may improve piscatorial good fortune but I don't recommend it. A change of bait would be a lot simpler.

Apologies if you've not received recent Cancer Times updates. It appears my computer also has a disease and deleted lots of addresses.

As I am still keen to explore alternative cancer remedies I have experimented with bathing in estuary mud. I'm now convinced that this could be the way forward. It smells awful!

PS. Most of my friends have already rushed off to their GP for a prostate test. If you haven't done so and you're over 50 give it a go. Don't be afraid of the digital rectal examination, it's actually the best bit of the whole process and it's free. This service is not available to women.

* Since this was written my friend Bridget has died in St. Joseph's. On my several visits I was very impressed with the place.

hopefully recovering. Tim sat there drawing it all.

It turns out that one has some choice where to receive palliative care – home, hospital and hospice seem to be the favourites. I was cheerily informed that I was fortunate as my nearest hospice is St. Joseph's* on Mare St. within crawling distance. What luck! I wonder if palliative care could be provided in a pub?

Recent news is quite good. The pathology test report says that the cancer has not spread to the lymph nodes and is not present in surrounding tissue. It also says that the tumour has passed 1 mm beyond the gland – not so good. Having seen a doctor and the surgeon in the past few days it is uncertain whether this means there are cancer cells still in the area. This will be informed by my next PSA test at the end of October.

The tumour was quite large, filling the left side of the prostate and half of the right side. The doctor I saw seemed genuinely surprised and happy at the result. They reckon that the cancer had been there for up to 5 years - with no symptoms.

After receiving this heartening news I took a stroll to the Hunterian Museum on Lincoln's Inn Fields where I celebrated by watching a couple of short films. The first showed the interior view of a prostate operation in which the gland was carved up using a heated wire loop and flushed out of the bladder in bits. The B film, which was much more exciting, featured the removal of a brain tumour. On the way out I had a chat with the man running the museum shop who turned out to be a recently retired prostate surgeon. He pointed out that although the da Vinci machine

SPECIMEN(S) RECEIVED:
A: Radical prostatectomy
B: Pre-prostatic fat
C: Left obturator Lymph node
D: Right obturator Lymph node
E: Right obturator Lymph node

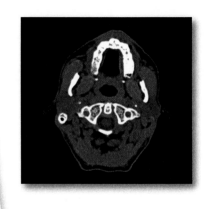

CLINICAL DATA:
PSA 20. Gleason 4+3. Radical prostatectomy.

MACROSCOPIC DESCRIPTION:
A. A radical prostatectomy specimen weighing 53g. The specimen is inked right side blue, left side black.
The specimen is divided at 5mm intervals from apex to base, 1-7. The greatest dimension is 5.5 cm, at level 5.
B. Pre-prostatic fat: Fatty tissue measuring 35 x 15 x 5 mm. All processed in one cassette.
C. Left obturator lymph node: Fibrofatty tissue measuring 35 x 30 x 10 mm including lymph nodes. All processed.
D. Right obturator lymph node: No tissue was received.
E. Right obturator lymph node: Fibrofatty tissue measuring 45 x 14 x 10 mm containing lymph nodes. All processed. (MP)

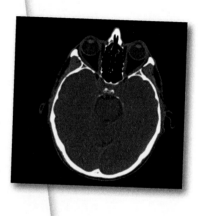

MICROSCOPIC DESCRIPTION:
A1. Adenocarcinoma Gleason 3+4, 1.4cm2, right and left side, gland confined.
Apical inked limit is (just) free of tumour.
A2. Adenocarcinoma Gleason 3+4, 3.1cm2, right and left side, specimen confined,
tumour extends beyond the gland for 1mm at right posterior but is clear of the circumferential inked surgical limit.
A3. Adenocarcinoma Gleason 3+4, 2.7cm2, right and left side, gland confined.
A4. Adenocarcinoma Gleason 3+4, 2.5cm2, right and left side, specimen confined,
tumour extends beyond the gland for 1mm at right posterior but

Head scans

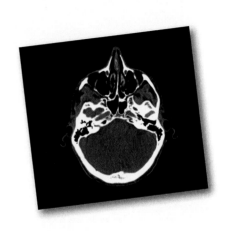

68

The white areas on the sections show where the cancer is

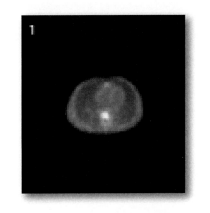

is clear of the
circumferential inked surgical limit.
A5. Adenocarcinoma Gleason 4+3, 1.5cm2, right and left side, gland confined.
A6. Adenocarcinoma Gleason 3+4, 0.5cm2, right side, gland confined.
A7. Carcinoma not identified. Basal inked limit, seminal vesicles and vasa are free of tumour.

B. Sections show pre-prostatic fat is free of tumour.

C. Sections show a total of 5 left obturator lymph nodes are free of tumour.

D. No tissue was received.

E. Sections show a total of 8 right obturator lymph nodes are free of tumour.

HISTOLOGICAL DIAGNOSIS:
Robotic radical prostatectomy: Adenocarcinoma Gleason 3+4 overall (maximal Gleason 4+3), volume 5.9ml, right and left side, specimen confined (stage pT3a).
Apical inked limit, basal inked limit, seminal vesicles and vasa are free of tumour. A total of 13 obturator lymph nodes are free of tumour.

ELECTRONICALLY SIGNED OUT BY:
DR A FREEMAN

REPORTED:
15/08/2012

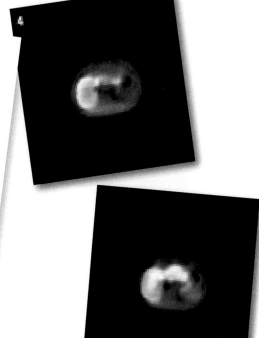

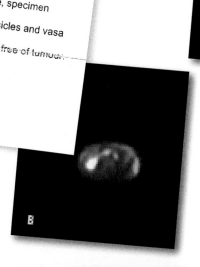

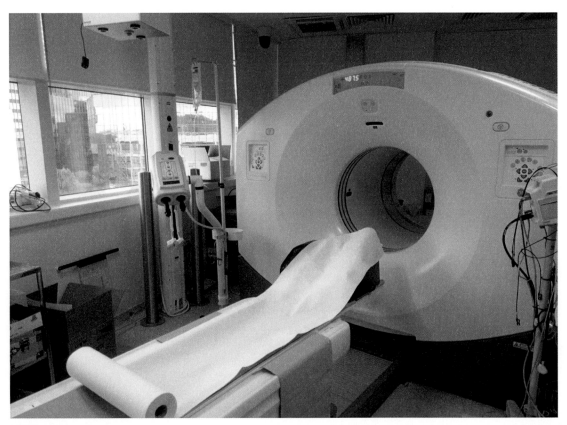

MRI Scanner

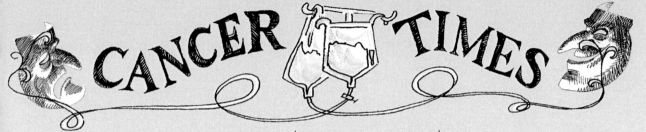
Thallophytic Pogonometry

Magnus Irvin

Many thanks to those who, having not received any recent correspondence, tactfully enquired whether I was dead. Well the latest news is I'm not. In fact I have just returned from taking Louise and my cancer on a trip around Andalucia.

On returning I visited the club-house for an appointment with the head oncologist, Professor Payne. My previous meeting was with the surgeon who assured me that he had removed the cancer and could "melt" any free cancer cells with an injection. This didn't go down well with the doctor who said he should stick to surgery. Her plan is to keep an eye on my PSA readings and decide whether to go for radiotherapy or continue to watch me. The latter sounds best as the RT is a 7-week course, 5 days per week with 6 months of hormone therapy. Looks like I may be wearing a dress again.

I was wearing one on the day I had my catheter removed and was whisked off straight from the Whittington Hospital to Whitstable for a charming day of beer and oysters (good source of zinc) courtesy of Dr. Ray.

Whilst he renewed the parking ticket I entered a pub on my own - the whole place went quiet. I'd forgotten what I looked like so I offered a friendly hello, doffed my floral hat, got the drinks and went outside where a bunch of decorators who had finished for the day stared at me. Eventually one of them came over and said they didn't see many men wearing dresses around those parts. I pointed out it was actually a djellaba. I also showed him my urinary leg bag after which we all got on quite well. I declined to mention I was also wearing a nappy.

Scrap value

I have been working on ways to help fellow sufferers and following the success of designer urinary leg bags I have started on a range of seaweed wigs and beards for those with chemotherapy side effects. I already have one customer. This thallophytic service can be offered to non-sufferers. The wigs are trés elegant, cheap and service is totally discreet.

Following detailed blood and urine tests, my witchdoctor* discovered I have high levels of heavy metals in me including cadmium, lead and mercury. I assume this is due to years of working with paints and inks.

According to a recent Nano SMT scan I also have raised levels of platinum and gold. If I do kick the bucket the corpse could have a decent scrap metal value.

However, from information found on the internet it seems likely that cancer can be cured by taking cannabis. Not sure how it works but it appears that bowel cancer can be helped by smoking ordinary cigarettes. Taking aspirins also does the job along with flax oil, blue scorpion venom and drinking your own urine. Of course, all of these cures have been suppressed by governments under pressure from profitable drug-making companies.

Armed with all my new-found knowledge I feel I could write a learned book on the subject or at least a daft article for the Lancet.

Anyway, I'm still alive and feeling fine. I hope you are.

The naturopath I visit for alternative treatment and advice. More details on P124.

In the Blue Oyster.

Statistics from Prostate Cancer UK 2018

CANCER TIMES

Tuesday 23rd October 2012 | magnusirvin.com/cancerweekly | No 8

NEW GIFT IDEAS FOR CHRISTMAS

More Decisions

Magnus Irvin

Sorry about this edition coming hard on the heels of number 7. If I don't watch out it may become a weekly.

Talking to my doctor last week I was interested to note that even if the cancer does move to another part of the body it is still prostate cancer. Particularly odd as I no longer have one.

Amongst other trials available to prostate cancer patients there is one I am signed up for that explores a genetic link for this type of cancer. On the form I had to give permission for them to use my removed prostate. The form states that there is no payment for this desirable item and it has to be classed as a "gift". Who can imagine a more delightful present? Perhaps it could be preserved until Christmas.

I also attended a physiotherapy session in the 52 Club on Gower St. It turned out that I was about the youngest person there and

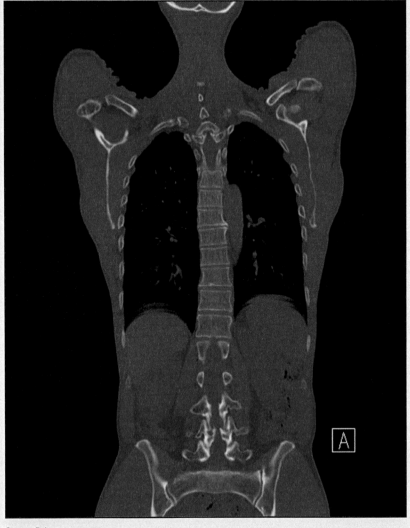

Spare Ribs

The ideal gift this Christmas

one of the few that could walk without assistance. I don't think the physio helped much but it was great for self-esteem.

PS. You can ignore last week's CT which stated that taking high doses of aspirin and smoking cannabis can cure cancer. It may be so but side effects include internal bleeding and talking cobblers.

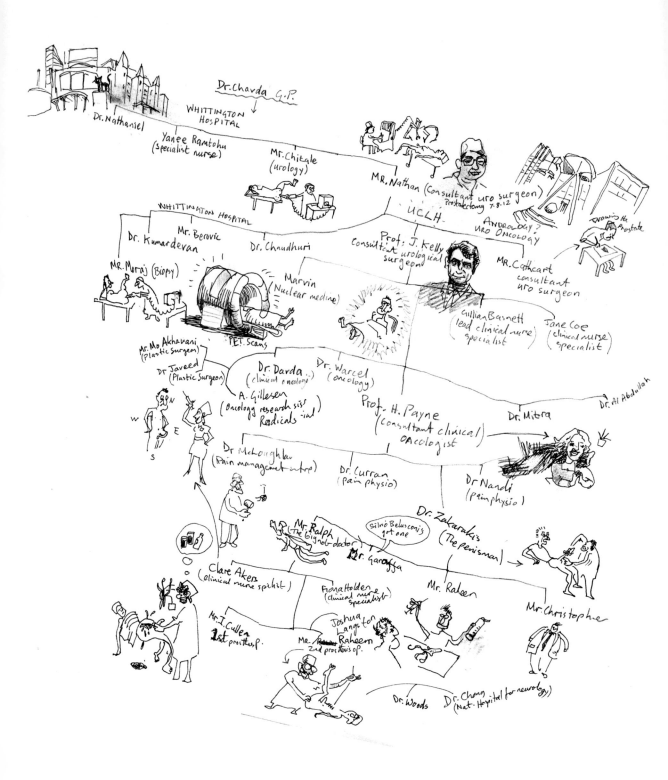

My medical family tree

CHAPTER 3
Rehabilitation

As I had been forewarned, it was no longer possible for me to have a spontaneous erection after the prostatectomy so I was referred to the urology department where I was shown the options available for less natural forms of penis inflation. Having tried strong doses of Viagra and Cialis without success I now had the choice between injection, vacuum pump and a prosthetic implant. A nurse showed me how to use a syringe to inject my penis and left the room as the drug took effect. Sure enough my stubborn appendage expanded into a fully formed erection but all was not well as the penis now had a pronounced 75 degree bend at the base which after some experimentation proved to be useless for sexual intercourse.

I was confused. Where had this deformity come from? On my next visit I was whipped off to see a specialist who after some painful prodding quickly diagnosed Peyronie's disease. He explained that this could be cured with a sort of nip & tuck operation but it would result in shortening of the penis. I decided against this, preferring to give the vacuum pump device a go.

The process involved inserting the penis into a plastic cylinder from which the air is removed by a built-in hand pump. It works by sucking the penis into the tube causing it to fill with blood. When the desired effect is attained a rubber ring is rolled from the tube on to the base of the penis, the vacuum released and an erect member emerges. I was sent home with a letter to my GP and masses of paperwork to add to my burgeoning library of all things urological, oncological and scatological. My GP of over 15 years was totally baffled by the letter and reluctantly gave me a prescription whilst informing me that I had become too expensive and perhaps it was time I changed to a surgery closer to where I lived.

University College London Hospitals **NHS**

NHS Foundation Trust

HP/uas/**40656302** NHS number: **4564092235**
11/08/2015

The Department of Oncology
1st Floor Central, UCLH
250 Euston Road
LONDON
NW1 2PG

Telephone: 0845 155 5000 ext 79287
Direct Line: 020 3447 9287
Fax: 020 3447 9055

Clinical Team PA: Susan Fennell
susan.fennell@uclh.nhs.uk

Clinic: HAP3A.Clinical Oncology. 05.08.15

Dr MFA Cahill
London Fields Medical Centre
38-44 Broadway Market
Hackney
London
E8 4QJ

Dear Dr Cahill,

Mr Magnus Irvin dob: 06/12/1952
17a Ellingfort Road, , London E8 3PA

Diagnosis:	**Gleason 4+3 locally advanced prostate cancer** **Presenting PSA 68** **TRUS biopsy Gleason 4+3 12 out of 12 cores** **MRI prostate T3a disease.** **No evidence of metastases on bone scan** **PET scan - ? solitary node.**
Treatment:	**radical robotic prostatectomy 7.8.2012 – histology shows Gleason 4+3 pT3a** **(1mm) bilateral disease, 13 obturator nodes were clear.** **Close monitoring of PSA for early salvage radiation if required**

It was a pleasure to meet with Mr Irvin in the oncology clinic at UCH today. I am pleased to report that he is generally well and that his PSA is stable 0.04. He has no new urinary nor bowel problems to report today and we will continue to monitor him on a three monthly basis.

Mr Irvin is very pleased with the penile implant which is working well but he is now due to have a hernia repair under the care of Mr Ralph's team.

I will look forward to seeing him again in three months time with an up to date PSA blood test but he knows he can contact me should he have any worries or concerns in the interim.

With kind regards and very best wishes.

Yours sincerely

Professor Heather Payne FRCR FRCP
Consultant Clinical Oncologist

uclh

University College Hospital	National Hospital for Neurology and Neurosurgery	Eastman Dental Hospital	Royal National Throat, Nose and Ear Hospital	Heart Hospital	Royal London Hospital for Integrated Medicine

CANCER TIMES

Sunday 13th January 2013 | magnusirvin.com/cancerweekly | No 9

PENIS REHAB

It's In Your Hands

Magnus Irvin

To help deal with the varied information I receive I have now divided my consultants into Dr. Goodnews and Dr. Badnews. One one side we have the possibility that the cancer has been removed and on the other that it is waiting to set up shop somewhere else in my body.

Attention has now been shifted to restoring my penis to working mode. There's nothing like a prostatectomy to cause problems in the lower regions. I was given a helpful booklet imaginatively titled 'In Your Hands'. It seems the options include pills, pumps, injections and implants. As a starter I have a 3-month course of Cialis which has so far given me firm, red ears.

Since being diagnosed I've read numerous books about fighting cancer with diet, fitness and alternative therapies. The one thing they all have in common is that everything one likes to eat,

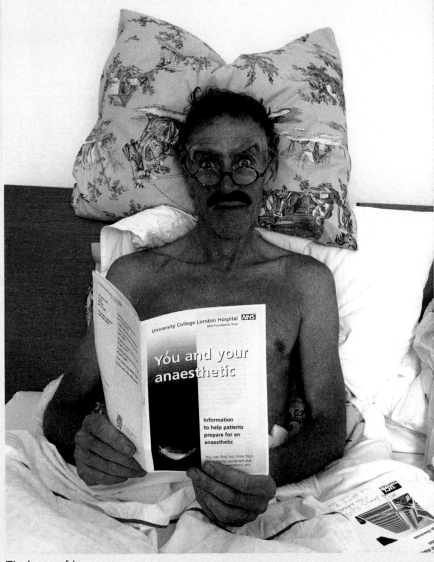

That's not a false nose

Dr Goodnews & Dr Badnews

drink and do is taboo. Given that us desperate types will try anything I am thinking of writing a self-help book called 'Curing Cancer with Beer'. It may not be scientific but who cares – I bet it would sell loads.

That's it really. Cancer and its after-effects may not be very nice but it's certainly not boring and it's all on the National Health.

Remember to get your prostate checked chaps.

Oh, and by the way, my Gleason score has now changed from 4+3 to 3+4. Isn't that interesting?

CANCER TIMES

Wednesday 6th March 2013 | magnusirvin.com/cancerweekly | No 10

Limp Bikers Without Prostates On Drugs

Magnus Irvin

It seems that the exciting phase of cancer treatment has passed and I am now in a watch and wait situation. After a year, if all is well I will have a PSA test every 6 months which will continue for as long as I last. I hope that the PSA level will not change as a slow rise will suggest that the cancer is still present probably in the ex-prostate site and a more rapid rise that it has metastasised to another location.

The test results last Tuesday showed that although the PSA had risen slightly to 0.04 it was still considered to be undetectable and nothing to worry about. Hmm!

My appointment to see Dr. Goodnews at the Whittington was changed as he is still ill and I saw the unfortunately named Dr. Dhai. It reminded me of some of my previous visits to this hospital many years ago, due mainly to motorbike accidents, when I noticed parking bays reserved for Dr. De'Ath and Dr. Strange. Are doctors chosen for their appropriate names?

Stiff Red Ears

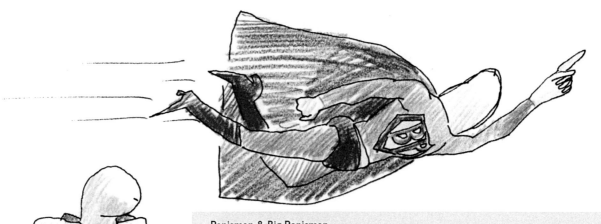

Penisman & Big Penisman

Anyway, I've decided not to have radiotherapy and have bought a motorbike instead.

I now appear to have 3 specialist nurses. They are all very good when you can actually get hold of them and given the amount of patients they see, I am amazed that they can remember who I am (apart from the one who calls me Martin).

One of my nurses sent me to the Macmillan Clubhouse to see an andrologist (male version of gynaecologist). As I sat in the bright and spacious waiting area an old chap clutching a walking stick let out an enormous belch that resounded through the large atrium. Then my name came up on the screen and I went upstairs to see the nob doctor for further discussion concerning the Peyronie's mystery. At a subsequent meeting I found that he is actually called the Penis Man by his colleagues – sounds more professional I suppose. Penis Man referred me to another doctor but once again the referral got lost and I'm now being re-referred to the main consultant andrologist, Dr. Ralph, who I assume is called Big Penis Man. He's the one to see if you want to know about pumps, pills, injections and implants. Meanwhile I'm still maintaining my big, red ears with daily Cialis.

I was also referred to a penis pump specialist who showed me a vacuum pump device. He assured me that may also straighten it. All I have to do is use it regularly. When I explain that this can all be fixed with an implant or a bit of pleating he asks who gave me that advice. On finding out he says "A surgeon would say that. They like to have people to practise on".

Anyway, having decided not to have radiotherapy I bought a motorbike instead. One of Dr. Badnews's team says that'll probably kill me first. I think he's jealous because his wife won't let him have one. Strangely he was almost right as a year or so later I crashed into the side of a skip lorry sustaining numerous injuries.

PS. Pelvic floor exercises are coming on a treat and I can now open oysters with my anus.

* Following a scooter accident, I recently had to visit Kasih Ibu Hospital in Bali where the radiologist, Dr. Dyah, added to my list of phonetically appropriate doctors that already includes doctors Dhai and Payne.

Statistics from Prostate Cancer UK 2018

Why had the Peyronie's appeared following the prostatectomy? The da Vinci machine had not operated directly in that area, as it removed the prostate through a slit above my navel and all other entrance points were in my upper abdomen. Why, after the operation, was my penis and scrotum so heavily bruised? I assumed that whatever had caused that trauma was also responsible for the Peyronie's disease but despite asking on numerous occasions I discovered that the doctors of the surgical department were unwilling to offer explanations.

After some perseverance it became clear that the vacuum device was having no effect on the curve so I decided to give the last option a go – the Titan OTR penile implant.

In September 2014 I had a 2-hour operation to insert the device. I woke to find myself once again in a hospital bed surrounded by the now familiar scenario of catheter, drain, tubes, urine and blood bags. Still under the influence of the anaesthetic I pulled back the sheets to find that the device had been fully inflated and I had an erection bound up in a ball of crepe bandage. A blue tube was sticking out of the end of my penis which itself was sticking out of the bandages. It looked like a white coconut with a strawberry on top. There was a big blood clot where the catheter emerged and a couple of blobs of super glue on either side. There was also a stitched incision on my right abdomen where the reservoir was inserted and I could just about make out a 3-inch incision across my scrotum replete with numerous stitches and lots more super glue. It all looked very unappetising and was extremely uncomfortable.

It was even more uncomfortable the next day when the surgeon visited to unwrap and deflate my penis, a procedure that involved gripping the pump housed in my lacerated scrotum whilst squeezing my penis to force the saline solution out of the tubes. A tearful procedure guaranteed to override the effect of all medication and return one to full sobriety. Getting any use out of it seemed a long way off. However, regular doses of painkillers and tea made it bearable.

Saturday 19th April 2014 | magnusirvin.com/cancerweekly | No 11

Trousers For Squid

Magnus Irvin

After a brief spell of not much to report the world of prostate cancer has once again entered an active stage.

Returning from holiday I went for a check-up that showed my PSA reading had risen again which

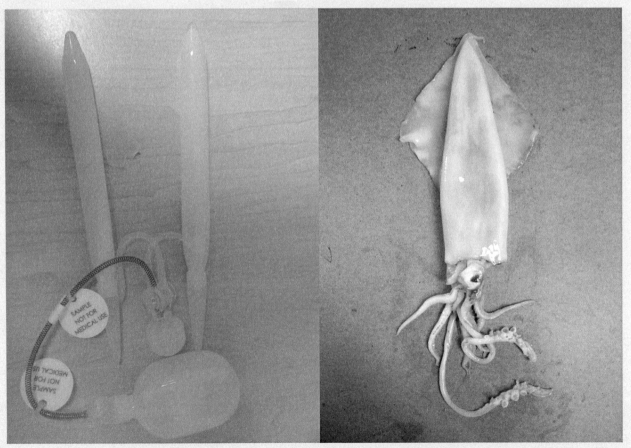

Squid **Implant**

Free tattoos on the NHS

probably means that the cancer has not been eradicated with the operation and that it is growing. When I asked the doctor about a prognosis he assured me I'd probably last until the end of the next fishing season, so all's well for now.

Unfortunately the Induratio Penis Plastica (Peyronie's disease) persists and a banana-shaped appendage has few uses short of somewhere to hang your hat. My efforts with the vacuum device proved fruitless as it had no effect on the Peyronie's disease and involved the use of some rather painful elastic bands that brought to mind the sort that farmers use to strangle sheeps' tails until they fall off. I believe this is known as an elastrator.

However, help is at hand with the all new Coloplast Titan Touch Zero penile prosthesis which is a surgically inserted implant. At my last appointment I was referred to a specialist nurse who threw what looked like a dead squid on the table and told me it would fix the problem. This fascinating, slightly irridescent silicone device utilises a couple of expansion chambers, a pump and saline reservoir to provide engorgement. 6 weeks after the quick operation the recipient will be able to inflate at any time. It works by pumping the saline solution into the chambers housed in the penis until the desired affect is achieved. I did ask if I could have any size I wanted but was

told that was their decision. In case of breakdown you are also provided with a bike pump and puncture repair kit. The Italian consultant assures me that Silvio Berlusconi has one. Roll on the Bunga Bunga parties.

Good news! There appears to be an unexpected bonus with radiotherapy - I get a free tattoo thrown in. This is in the form of some small, permanent dots on the abdomen that help the radiographer to aim the ray gun at the right place. So what with living in London Fields and having a beard I may soon have some tattoos so then I'll be even more trendy. Nearly forgot to mention. I was given a copy of the Bristol Stool Chart so that I could classify my stools. Fascinating!

Bristol Stool Chart

Since it can be hard to state what is normal and what is abnormal, some health professionals use a scale to classify the type of stool passed. This helps assess how long the stool has spent in the bowel.

Type 1 has spent the longest time in the bowel and type 7 the least time. A normal stool should be a type 3 or 4, and depending on the normal bowel habits of the individual, should be passed once every one to three days.

Type 1		Separate hard lumps, like nuts (hard to pass)
Type 2		Sausage shaped but lumpy
Type 3		Like a sausage but with cracks on the surface
Type 4		Like a sausage or snake, smooth and soft
Type 5		Soft blobs with clear cut edges (passed easily)
Type 6		Fluffy pieces with ragged edges, a mushy stool
Type 7		Watery, no solid pieces, entirely liquid

Image reproduced by kind permission of Dr K Heaton, Reader in Medicine, University of Bristol.

www.bladderandbowelfoundation.org
Email: help@bladderandbowelfoundation.org | Telephone: 01926 357220

Registered office address: Pegasus House, Solihull Business Park, Solihull, West Midlands, United Kingdom, B90 4GT. Company number: 10377236. Registered in the UK

91

Within a couple of months when most of the pain had gone I was able to use the penis implant and was pleased to find that the inflatable tubes were able to straighten the curve of the Peyronie's disease.

So there I was with a functioning penis, numerous new scars and a nagging uncertainty as to whether I still had cancer. I still had not told my parents and it was shortly after my diagnosis that my mum was hospitalised following a fall. It soon became clear to me that each time there was a change in my illness she would suffer another setback. After a continual series of mishaps she eventually developed infections and dementia and I found that I spent time visiting her in various hospitals whilst recovering from my own problems. It was as if we had a private competition going on. Sometimes she would look at me and say, "There will never be anything wrong with you. You're invincible". Little did she know.

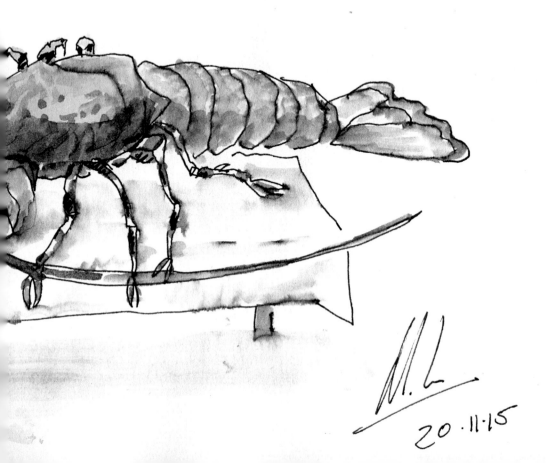

20·11·15

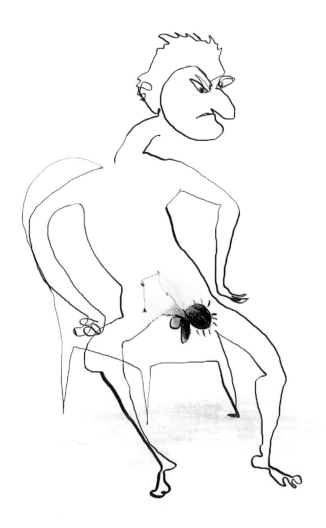

Starbucks Offer New Coffee Experience

Magnus Irvin

My witchdoctor has excelled himself recently. In an attempt to get my zinc level up he is using alchemy. Tiny amounts of brown powder in 30 small, folded paper packages is mixed with butter and washed down with milk. Alchemical zinc takes 3 months to prepare and is the end product of continual distillations. There is so little of it in each envelope that it's hard to see. He also gave me a session of acupuncture, jabbing fat needles into the back of my knees until the blood running out of the veins formed puddles around my feet. This was in order to get rid of toxic blood which gathers there. Mine was, of course, quite pure and required very little letting.

Also, in the interests of personal, internal hygiene and perversion I visited a colonic irrigator, something that had been on my "things to do before you die" list for some time. It was nowhere near as exciting as I'd hoped but she did have some interesting insights

Coffee Break

into my diet and intestines based on what came out. She told me I was very good at it and she'd never known anyone hold so much water on their first visit. There's something to be proud of ! A natural talent with few uses. She recommended that on my next visit

I could try a coffee enema.

Over the past 6 weeks most of my family including mum, dad and son have been in hospital. I have spent more time delivering and visiting them than I spend there looking after myself and I'm beginning to

unsure what that meant and the curse would not be lifted until the 33 days were up. However, he did say that the ceremony was a success and any bad spirits or succubus should have been removed by now. It did not mean that they would not come back.

Well that's it really. Probably be something gruesome to report with disgusting photos in a couple of weeks.

Yours, full of wind and water

Magnus

PS. I came across another fine example of alternative treatments in the online Guardian -

A recent study from the University of Exeter has been reported as showing that smelling farts can cure cancer, as well as many other diseases. The study claimed that targeted delivery of a compound called AP39 causes more hydrogen sulphide to be produced by an ailing cell, and hydrogen sulphide in small doses can prove protective to the cell's mitochondria, which supplies the cell's energy and is often damaged by diseases. Hydrogen sulphide preventing this mitochondrial damage therefore can help cells resist the progression of many diseases.

Sounds like a simple home remedy.

---

think that my thunder has been stolen by these thoughtless relatives – don't they know it's ME who's ill? My mum who was re-admitted to hospital following a fall certainly doesn't as she's now not sure if my name is Sainsbury, Turtle or Rabbit. It's sad but entertaining.

However, in a subconscious effort to regain the limelight I made a valiant attempt to redress the balance. Whilst waiting at London Fields station for the 19.16 to Liverpool Street I decided to practise my dizzy exercises and see how far I could walk along the platform with my eyes closed. After 25 steps I fell off on to the rails. No train was coming but I was back on the platform in a shot nursing a few bumps. My knee still hurts due to pulled ligaments and that was 10 weeks ago. I'll stick to practising near rivers.

When my son heard about my latest transport-related altercation (I had

recently been struck on the head by a bus when my bicycle slipped on ice, crashed my motorbike into a skip lorry and bashed my head on a canal bridge) he decided to seek the help of a recommended witchdoctor in Indonesia. He found the man in Java specialising in Ruqya (an Islamic form of exorcism) who told him I had been cursed – possibly by accident. Yusef, the healer, used Finbarr as a channel to get to me whilst also referring to the only photo I could provide of myself on a motorbike. After rubbing themselves in oil that had been blessed by an elder healer they laid on the floor in a tiny smoke-filled room and were covered in white sarongs. After a long period of mutterings and a shower of petals the ceremony was over and Yusef said he would pray for me over the next 33 days. A week later I was knocked off my bicycle by a Triumph Bonneville motorbike but Yusef said he was

"It goes up your bum, through the rectum
and bites chunks out of your prostate gland"

CANCER TIMES

Wednesday 12th November 2014 | magnusirvin.com/cancerweekly | **No 13**

Four's a Crowd

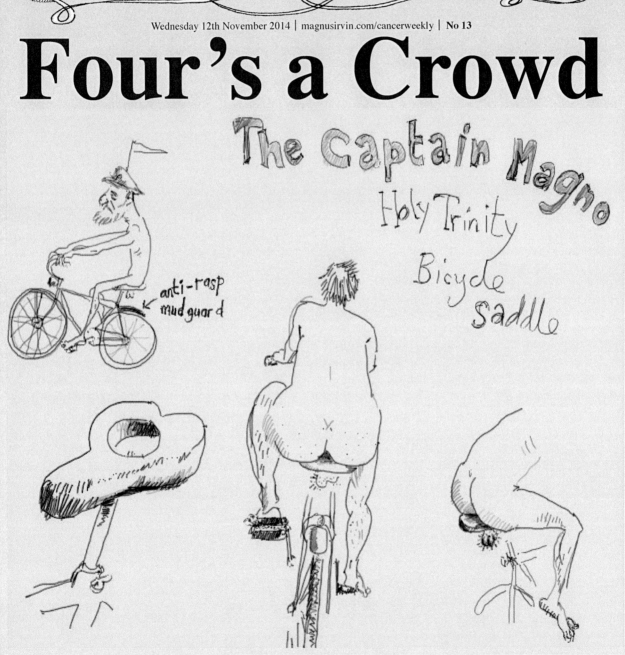

The Captain Magno

Holy Trinity Bicycle Saddle

anti-rasp mudguard

Magnus Irvin

This week, the world of prostate cancer opens windows on to new horizons of discomfort. Having just returned from a session of torture in the urology department I have cancelled this afternoon's appointments in favour of sitting at home with my private parts immersed in a bowl of warm rice pudding.

Since the insertion of the Coloplast Titan* contraption there are now 3 items jostling for space in my scrotum and it has become rather uncomfortable. It appears that the small pump has become attached to my right testicle. Big Penis Man in the urology department assures me that he can sort this out but I will have to wait a while.

However, in general things are fine and I can now cycle short distances if I position my bum to one side of the saddle. Ideally a saddle with a hole in the middle would be desirable.

Just as a matter of interest, so that I could inform my son when he will inherit my impressive estate, I checked out a couple of online death-date sites. I am now satisfied to know that I will die on 19/2/25 or 20/5/36. I wonder what odds I'd get on a bet?

In a further attempt to steal my thunder, my mum whose dementia is increasing has now expressed a desire to eat her clothes and discusses possible ways of cooking coats and socks. I reckon she deserves her own TV cookery programme. Can only be more fun than the majority of them. So until a gripping report of further interventions and realignments, goodbye and stay well.

Catheters akimbo.

This erection device is marvellously named after the Titans, a bunch of Greek mythological deviants that specialised in castration, incest and child-devouring as well as giving birth to the equally degenerate Olympian gods. The charming Cronos actually emasculated his father Uranus. (no sniggering at the back please.)

CHAPTER 4
Self Help

As soon as I knew I had cancer I researched all the self-help methods I could get my hands on and found myself confronted with huge amounts of information much of which was contradictory and unproven. Complementary cancer therapies are many and varied but the basis of all of them is the strengthening of the immune system and the cleansing of toxins from the body.

The immune system is a powerful tool against infection but once it is compromised the door is open to problems. Most anti-cancer advice focuses on diet and the use of supplements and complementary medicines. Toxins in the body may have built up over a number of years and can be hard to identify and eradicate. If the immune system is occupied in fighting against them then it is not able to focus fully on protecting against other infections including free radicals that damage healthy cells and put further strain on our natural protection mechanisms.

Making sense of this labyrinth of confusing new information was proving difficult so I took the advice of a friend who had survived throat cancer and contacted a health practitioner that he recommended. It was a good move.

Health advice

Philip Weeks is a naturopath, herbalist and acupuncturist with clinics in Hereford and London. He specialises in detoxification and has a major interest in mercury poisoning and vaccination damage. At our first meeting he stressed the importance of boosting the immune system and controlling inflammation. He also helped make sense of all the information I had accumulated. To get an overall picture of my state of health he sent me for detailed blood analysis at a private clinic. The results were interesting, revealing that I had a high level of cadmium as well as very low levels of vitamin D

and zinc. Each of these could be contributing factors regarding my cancer. It is known that zinc and vitamin D are both effective in protection of the prostate but it was the presence of cadmium that really rang alarm bells. Cadmium is a heavy metal that the body has no mechanism for expelling – it is more toxic than mercury and harder to get rid of as it attaches itself to your DNA and affects every body cell. It occupies the immune system to such an extent that it neglects to protect other areas such as the prostate. It also depletes zinc and vitamin D. This, combined with a history of prostate cancer in my family may go some way to explaining why I got it (or did it get me?) It was clear that the cadmium had to go.

Mr. Weeks began treating me for cadmium poisoning using various natural remedies. Over a period of 2 years the cadmium was eradicated by a gradual process of chelation. However, further blood tests for DNA adducts

revealed the presence of malondialdehyde* and some sulphur-based adducts, both known carcinogens. Following continued chelation these were removed within a year. Better off without that lot.

It would be nice to say that was the problem sorted out but further urine tests showed a similarly high amount of mercury and lead (more than three times the safe limit of both) so the chelation work continued. It's hard to say where these metals came from, possibly a lifetime of spraying large quantities of paint and many years using printmaking inks and solvents. However I had acquired that exotic range of metals, it made me feel better to know that they had been identified and we were dealing with them.

I now take daily supplements of zinc and vitamin D to redress the balance. Using the service of a naturopath or other specialist means stepping outside of the

NHS into the private sector. It is not cheap but for me it was worth it.

* Which as you know is a naturally occurring product of lipid peroxidation and prostaglandin biosynthesis that is mutagenic and carcinogenic.

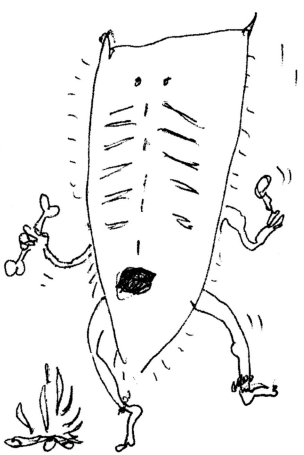

Welcome to

Anti-cancer diets

There is a huge amount of information available on anti-cancer diets. Endless books and websites are devoted to the subject. Much of it is common sense and a lot of it contradictory. The anti-cancer diet attaches as much importance to what you should not eat as to what you should. They usually advocate avoiding certain foods that are acidic, inflammatory or toxic and increasing intake of foods that are alkaline, anti-inflammatory, oxygenating and rich in antioxidants.

I decided it made sense to cut out all processed foods and reduce sugar intake as much as possible.* I also cut down on red meat, dairy, alcohol and white foods such as bread, rice and pasta. At the very least it made sense on a general health basis to cut down on obviously unhealthy foods and to step up the intake of fresh vegetables whilst avoiding any products that contain chemical additives. I even changed the soap, shampoo, sunscreen and toothpaste I used for those with natural ingredients. This may sound drastic but a lot of cosmetics contain unpleasant ingredients. Recently some sun-protection creams have been found to cause more skin problems than exposure to the sun. Also, despite some dentists insisting that amalgam fillings do not leak mercury I had my metal fillings replaced, (see X-ray on p.5).

the Labyrinth

But beware, once you start investigating this endless labyrinth of advice it is easy to get carried away. You could end up eating nothing. To start with I was living on green vegetables and not a lot more. At that time everything edible looked like poison, even an apple looked like a bag of sugar. Mind you it did help Louise lose weight and we both had delightful complexions. Also it pays to be sceptical. I recently read that a well-known health guru cited in many nutrition books has been banged up for fraud. I lost some weight but when I mentioned this to a doctor I was told not to worry as in cancer tests it was found that thin rats lasted longer than the fat ones.

* Cancer cells are far more adept at taking in sugar than ordinary cells. This is the basis of how the PET scan works - glucose and a radioactive material are combined and injected into the body, and since the cancer grabs the sugar before the healthy cells do it also takes in the radioactivity which shows up on the scan, revealing its location. Many sources say that sugar actually feeds the cancer, fuelling its growth, so all anti-cancer diets recommend cutting it out. Unfortunately sugar is found in many foods and drinks including fruit and beer.

Alternative therapies

I like to read about alternative therapies and the more outlandish they are the better.

Many organisations claim that cancer can be "cured" with natural products alone. Whilst this could be true I felt more secure relying on the established medical advice at the same time as acknowledging alternative methods. I have often heard that it is not in the interest of drug companies to investigate and test natural products from which they cannot profit, so little research funding is available. A lot is made of this by practitioners of alternative therapies and it is hard to know what is right, what is mad and what is a conspiracy theory.

There is much said about how both drug companies and alternative medicine providers apply pressure on doctors and the public to use their products, often citing spurious claims that have not been properly tested. Many "health supplements" are sold via advertising that convinces you to address problems that do not exist. George Orwell wrote that the true genius of advertising is to sell you the solution and the problem. That appears to be the case with so many independent clinics claiming to offer effective cancer treatments. A lot of these clinics can be found in Mexico claiming that they have

been hounded out of the USA by official medical organisations in the pay of the powerful drug companies. Many and varied treatments are offered with remedies based on high doses of vitamin C, flax oil, lycopene, pomegranates, saw palmetto, selenium, baking soda and cannabis oil.

The list goes on and research has shown that although not medically proven some of these natural products could be effective against cancer. Curcumin, a powerful anti-inflammatory rich in antioxidants, is the active ingredient of turmeric and is the subject of some current medical research. Clinical trials show it is effective against conditions including psoriasis, Alzheimer's disease, arthritis and possibly cancer. Some natural remedies even make a crossover between the traditional and alternative worlds of treatment. Iscador, a brand name for an extract of mistletoe, although considered a complementary therapy is now commonly used in oncology departments in German hospitals to boost the immune system. Tests show that it can extend the life of cancer patients (although for how long is difficult to ascertain). As always, it is up to the individual to follow what makes most sense to them and without proper clinical evidence it is difficult to decide.

Fortunately though, you will not have to go as far as Mexico for your cure since help is at hand in your local greengrocer's. A recent tabloid headline I saw read "Rhubarb cures cancer".

There is also a huge range of complementary therapies available from homeopathy to colonic irrigation. Interestingly a number of these are available in the integrated medicine department at the UCLH Macmillan centre which offers massages, reiki, reflexology, acupuncture and aromatherapy sessions to patients. I'm not sure what the surgeons think of this but if these sessions help relax you then why not?

How effective any of these treatments are is yet to be established but they do offer an interesting alternative to the 3 main approaches offered by the hospital – surgery, radiotherapy and chemotherapy, treatments that even the doctors admit can cause further cancers.

It really boils down to how far you want to go along the route of complementary and integrated medicine. In the area between the

treatments based on proper clinical evidence and New Age alternative nonsense there is a lot of information that is hard to verify. There are few people to ask who have an informed overview of the whole subject which is why talking to a health practitioner was useful to me. I did discuss it with my doctors but usually their attitude was that what you eat or take as supplements will make no difference. However, some supplements do not react well with regular hospital treatments so your doctors should be kept informed. Curcumin is an example as it can have serious effects combined with cytotoxic drugs. I am happy to know that the doctors who treated me are the best at what they do. I don't particularly want them to tell me about other treatments. If I want dietary advice I'll go somewhere else.

Practitioners of alternative treatments point out that both radio and chemotherapy are extremely damaging to the body and are often responsible for further cancers. Chemotherapy, in particular, attacks the immune system using drugs that are carcinogenic at a time when the immune system is so necessary to fight the cancer. They also point out that in many cases the cancer returns after therapy in a more aggressive form. Although many of the alternative methods claim success they also point out that their treatment will not be effective for everyone. So how do you find out? It's difficult.

CANCER TIMES

Wednesday 4th February 2015 | magnusirvin.com/cancerweekly | **No 14**

ANGRY DOCTOR LOSES PATIENTS

TESTICULAR ADHESION
For the man who has everything

INFLATION ON THE RISE

Magnus Irvin

2014 was not a particularly comfortable year for me, having spent most of it standing up. Then to cap it all my mum played her trump card and had a final stroke. She died in a care home a week before Christmas. I talked to her whilst she was in a coma and sang along to a CD of South Pacific. I think it's such a shame that I didn't tell her about my illness and won't have the opportunity again.

On the brighter side, I do now talk to my dad about it. We also appear to be competitive as he has 3 different cancers which he treats with large infusions of beer, red wine and whisky every evening. So effective is his treatment that he now has to sleep on the ground floor of his house as he can't get up the stairs at night. When I told him about my prostate cancer he replied, "Oh yes, I've got that one."

Magnus and Fin in search of witch doctors

I've taken to drinking too much again. It's not really that I decided to drink a lot but Christmas got in the way and I have been in New York for a while where it's hard not to indulge.

I am writing this in the Carlton Arms Hotel in Manhattan where my Surgical Dreams exhibition of prints is due to open on Friday. This is my favourite hotel, practically the last of its kind. Formerly an old flop house it retains all the crooked charm and steaming radiators that are now only seen in films. With each of its rooms decorated by different artists this is a great place to revel in a friendly Bohemian atmosphere. There are always artists staying here. My friend Heinz who was diagnosed with bladder and prostate cancers at the same time as me is here from Australia. Hugo who runs the place found out recently that he has prostate cancer, so along with a young writer living in the hotel whilst having radiotherapy for breast cancer we have formed a rather jolly Cancer Club that runs mainly on Malbec.

My Titan prosthesis prompted my friend Mr. Batchelor to ask if I'd ever fancied men. When I said not he suggested that I'd now be able to have sex with men as I could get an erection without any emotional stimulus. Of course a really adventurous recipient of this device could take this theory further and have sex with animals, food and even furniture. Some friends are very odd.

After a long-term battle to upstage me in the cancer stakes my dad died in July 2017 just before his 91st birthday. He had been moved to a care home where he preferred to drink whisky rather than anything they could offer. When he found himself gagging on his drink the staff kindly mixed a thickener with the whisky to help him swallow it. How thoughtful.

I am now working with my friend Nick to publish an illustrated book, both factual and personal, about my prostate cancer experience so it seems the right time to stop sending these updates particularly as I hope there will not be a lot more to tell in the future. I'll let you know when the book is available. It will be the perfect gift for the man in your life. Love and best wishes and many thanks for reading these messages.

CHAPTER 5

Radiotherapy

In April 2020 I went to the Macmillan Centre to give my usual blood sample. Whilst sitting at home that evening I received a phone call from an excited Professor Payne who said she couldn't wait until Wednesday to tell me that the PSA reading was undetectable and that as far as she was concerned the radiotherapy had been successful and I was now cancer-free. As phone calls go it was a good one.

To explain this sudden change of events I need to go back to where I left off.

....

On 27 March 2019 I had breakfast and took my daily dose of cannabis oil (medicinal purpose) before setting off for a consultation at the Macmillan Centre. My PSA had been rising steadily over the past 6 months and I was concerned.

At the meeting I was told that my reading had gone from 0.14 to 0.17 within 3 months, the most rapid rise since the prostatectomy. The doctor invited Professor Payne into our meeting and we discussed radiotherapy. I was very disappointed that it had come to this but it now appeared to be the best way forward.

The meeting passed in a blur and it was not until we got into the foyer that I realised I was completely stoned. I had made the cannabis mixture far too strong (again). Fortunately Louise was with me and we ran through what had been talked about in the meeting whilst waiting at the pharmacy for a 6 months' supply of bicalutamide. My previous experience with these tablets had not been very enjoyable with side-effects that included hot flushes, itchy skin and gynaecomastia (breast enlargement). Longer-term hormone therapy can be more serious, possibly leading to high blood pressure, heart attack, strokes and diabetes.

Having decided to accept this treatment I visited the radiotherapy department in the basement of UCH for the Radiotherapy Education Seminar. A small group of men sat silently in a windowless room listening to the occasional rumble of a passing tube train before watching a presentation that explained all aspects of the treatment. I was due for 66 Gy radiotherapy to the prostate bed area in 33 fractions over a period of 7 weeks, 2 Gy each day. Afterwards we chatted whilst waiting for our prescriptions. There was plenty to talk about including linear accelerators, multi-leaf collimators and further interesting side-effects.

The prescriptions provided us each with a pack of micro-enemas for use in the 5 days leading up to the planning CT scan. These are self-administered and clear the bowel for the important scan that will determine the exact position on the scanner bed to be used for treatment on all subsequent visits.

The bowel needs to be empty so that the prostate area is in the same position for each visit. This means that an enema has to be used every time before each radiotherapy session. Another requirement is the drinking of 900 ml. of water 40 minutes before the scan. This is to expand the bladder and push the bowels away from the area of treatment.

To get my body in exactly the same position on the machine every day three dots were permanently tattooed onto both sides and the middle point of my abdomen. The technicians use these to move you into position on the bed, guided by a cross-hairs point projected from the machine. This is still only an approximate position as the final adjustment is done with reference to the initial planning scan. Once positioned you must remain completely still as the computer-controlled scanner bed makes minor adjustments to get you exactly aligned. It is amazingly accurate.

On my first visit for treatment to the radiotherapy department I arrived at midday. Having used the enema and drunk the water I sat there in a dull, boring room for over an hour. It was quite unpleasant. Another patient's friend opposite me was talking non-stop and much too loud whilst I was struggling to hold on to a full bladder. Then I realised that to cap it all Whitney Houston was playing on a continuous loop through the waiting-room speakers. As I entered the room that housed the Linac B machine a young nurse asked if I was OK. I told her I was not. I was uncomfortable and Whitney Houston was driving me mad. I had no intention of entering this hospital with cancer and leaving with brain damage.

Most thoughtfully she asked what music I would prefer and off the top of my head I replied "The Beatles" which she immediately found on the treatment-room laptop.

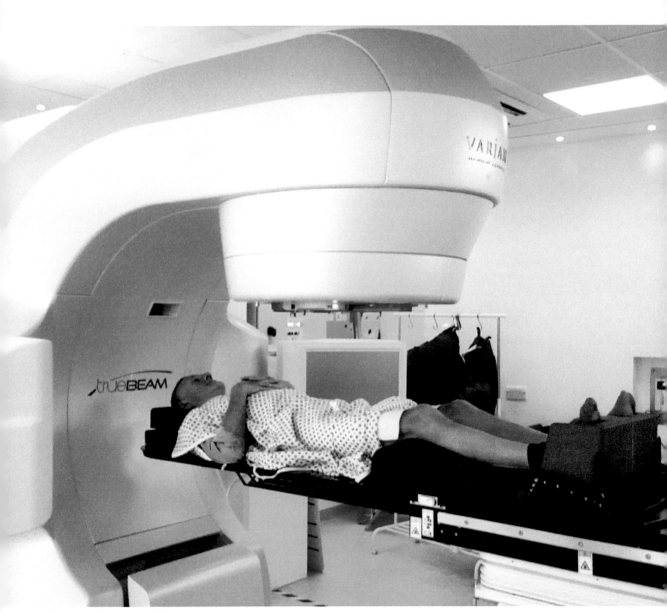

Linear accelerator machine

The machine that does the job is called a volumetric-modulated arc therapy machine (VMAT) and would look quite at home in any science fiction film. As you lie on it 3 bulky arms containing the ray gun and two scanners swing forward around your reclining body. When the process begins the arms revolve around you first in a clockwise then an anti-clockwise direction. With some imagination it can feel like the machine is static and it is you who is spinning. As the machine is doing its job the bed occasionally repositions itself with small adjustments. On this first occasion the whole process took about 25 minutes but this included some more scans. Most of my following visits were much shorter. Usually I would be in and out of the hospital within 15 minutes.

On a later visit I discovered the room had a concealed lighting system. It wasn't long before I would turn up to be lead into the room with the Beatles already playing and the soft lights changing colour across the ceiling. What a service! I think they usually reserve the lights for children.

My treatment started on 26 June and ended on 9 August. I visited the department 33 times. To assist matters I was given my own surgical gown.

I soon worked out that if I had the earliest appointment I could carry out the majority of my preparation before leaving home. The schedule was the same every day. Get up at 6:40 am, use enema at 7:00 then go to the toilet 10 minutes later. Drink the water (5 glasses)

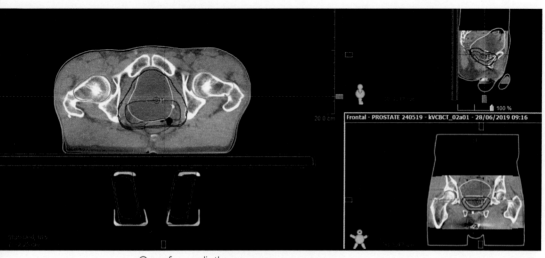

One of my radiotherapy scans

between 7:30 and 7:40 then catch the 7:50 train to Liverpool Street. That got me to the hospital at exactly the right time to put on my gown and go straight to the machine at 8:30 am. Despite feeling an urgent need to urinate I did fall asleep on many occasions as the arms of the machine revolved around me. Surprisingly, no matter how I felt on my way there I always left feeling great and full of energy. The department staff were absolutely superb and on my last day we had an emotional farewell. I gave them all a box of chocolate anuses. I had finally finished my term in a different world. With the strict schedule and daily commute on crowded trains it had been like having a proper 5-days-a-week job for a couple of months.

The week before the radiotherapy finished I met Professor Payne who said the success of the treatment could not be gauged for quite a while as the bicalutamide would continue to keep the PSA low even after the 6 months course finished in September. It would then be a further 6 months before a true reading could be obtained. She also pointed out that the radiotherapy does not actually kill the cancer cells but damages them so that they cannot reproduce and they die off at the end of their life cycle, "They're on death-row now". Fortunately the non-cancerous cells are able to grow back.

In December my test reported an undetectable PSA level of -0.01 but it was not until the same result in April 2020 that I felt able to believe that I no longer had cancer. After 8 years it was a good feeling. I was also encouraged to know that if cancer cells did remain they would probably have been detected now that my testosterone had returned to its normal level. My most recent results in August 2020 (once again delivered on the phone as all hospital meetings are off because of Covid-19) reported the same reading almost a year after the last radiotherapy treatment.

A list of Supplements and Remedies I have taken

The Linear Accelerator

External beam radiotherapy uses high doses of radiation to destroy cancer cells and shrink tumours. The machine does not touch the patient and no sensation can be felt during the treatment.

On entering the radiotherapy treatment room, known as a 'bunker', the patient is laid on a bed that is separate from the main machine. Therapeutic radiographers align the patient using lasers to get them in the correct position for treatment. The bed then moves into the correct position before treatment begins.

There are two large arms on the machine that move forward from behind the patient's head to the left and right of his/her body. One of these houses a camera and the other captures the images. These arms can also be used to make a mini CT scan. The images are used to check and adjust the position of the patient before the treatment begins.

The biggest arm, above the bed and between the two others, is the head which delivers the radiation. As the process begins, the arms and head begin to circle first clockwise then anti-clockwise around the bed in arcs. The patient remains completely still.

The linear accelerator delivers radiation in the form of mega-voltage X-rays. It initially uses a gun to make an electron which is fired the length of a long tube at the top of the machine. This electron is accelerated faster and faster along the tube until it reaches the desired speed, giving the machine its name 'linear accelerator'. Then it is bent downwards at a right-angle by powerful magnets. The electron is aimed at a tungsten disc which creates a reaction that converts it into a photon, an X-ray, which provides the radiation for the therapy. As the radioactive protons come down from the machine they are then shaped by four lead blocks into a square or rectangular profile. This beam is then further shaped, more accurately, by up to 40 pairs of multi-leaf collimators. These collimators are a series of small, lead

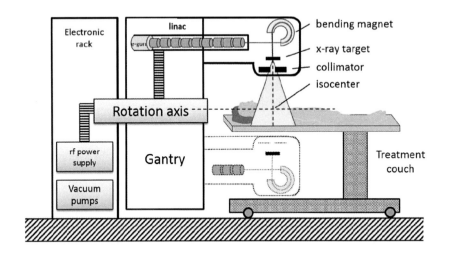

sticks that are constantly changing position as the machine moves around the body.

The changing profile of the radiotherapy beam is computer controlled to exactly match the shape of the target area for all angles from which it is fired. The intensity of the X-ray may also vary during treatment as the arms revolve – giving it the name Intensity Modulated Radiotherapy (IMRT). The radiation prescription is divided and given in small equal doses over a set period, known as 'fractions'.

Dividing the treatment up gives healthy cells a chance for some recovery between treatments to reduce side effects. The radiation damages the cancerous cells in two ways. Firstly, it can hit the DNA directly causing a 'double strand' break. Secondly, the radiation reacts with water in the body to create 'free radicals' that can also damage the structure of the DNA, causing eventual cell death.

In my experience this whole remarkable process took less than ten minutes.

EPILOGUE

Cancer is often talked about in vaguely military terms referring to the "battle" that one has to "fight" and a disease that must be "defeated". It is a measure of how dealing with cancer is perceived as a tough, physical confrontation. Those who have it are termed "sufferers" or "victims" and those who manage to beat it are "survivors". So far I am surviving.

Since the prostatectomy operation in 2012 my PSA readings gradually rose from their initial undetectable level. In 2016 the level dropped a couple of points to 0.04 giving me hope that the cancer may be diminishing, but by the end of that year it had risen to 0.06 and continued to do so until mid 2017 when it reached 0.09. The doctors had said that radiotherapy should be considered if it reached 0.1 and I fully expected to start treatment soon. However, my next reading dropped to 0.8 and there it stayed for 6 months. At this time my doctors were not sure if it was cancer or PSA produced by

healthy prostate cells left over from the operation. In 2019 the reading rose more rapidly to 0.17 and radiotherapy commenced.

When I think back I realise how fortunate it was that my cancer was discovered in the nick of time. In retrospect I was daft to have gone so long without a prostate check given that my dad had it for many years. It was a lucky day when I went to the GP and saw a locum doctor. It could have been very different had I seen my usual one who on a previous occasion recommended osteopathy for the same complaint. I subsequently found out that this new doctor had just returned from a conference about prostate cancer and was well informed on a full range of symptoms that fortunately included back ache. Some weeks afterwards I phoned and thanked her. She was really pleased.

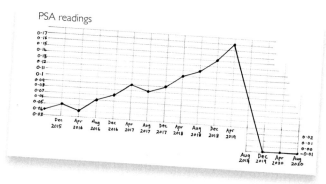

PSA readings

I have also been lucky to have the services of a modern hospital with sophisticated facilities and superb staff, as well as good health and nutrition advice. The whole process has been quite extraordinary and despite having been ill I have always felt fine and even healthy.

At all times I have had complete faith in the advice and treatments offered to me at the hospital and have not regretted any of the decisions made. Although on occasions confused, I have always been involved in the decision-making process and did what felt best at the time. I also see a lot of sense in combining traditional and complementary medicine. In my case getting the immune system on top form made a lot of sense. The body does have its own mechanisms to fight cancer so why not help it to give it its best shot?

I still take some supplements and adhere to a healthy diet.

With my PSA level back to undetectable levels I continue to explore anything that I think could help and to have faith in things that do not necessarily make sense. That is a concept that appeals to me. So I will persevere with my present regime including beer at weekends and the occasional cake whilst keeping an eye on the PSA. That, combined with the support of friends and family, is good medicine.

I hope that this book will help other men and their families to understand some aspects of the prostate cancer experience and to continue to enjoy life after diagnosis. I wish them the very best of luck with their treatment as well as good health and happiness – if that is not asking too much.

GLOSSARY

Chapter 1

PPSA Prostate specific antigen is a protein made by the prostate gland which naturally leaks out into the blood. The PSA test measures the amount of PSA in your blood and can give an indication of the presence of cancer.

Digital rectal examination A manual examination in which a doctor sticks his finger up your backside and feels the prostate gland through the rectum wall for unusual surface texture.

Prostate biopsy The trans rectal needle biopsy involves an ultrasound scanner guiding a plastic tube that is pushed up the rectum. A needle is then passed through the wall of the rectum into the prostate where it snips out 12 tissue samples.

T3 Staging is measured on a T scale of 1 to 4. T1 and T2 are known as localised prostate cancer. T3 and 4 are advanced and indicate that the cancer has spread beyond the gland into the surrounding tissue.

Bone scan A diagnostic imaging test to determine if cancer has spread to the skeleton. A small amount of radioactive tracer is injected into the bloodstream before the patient is laid in a scanner. With the aid of a gamma camera the resulting images can reveal the presence of prostate cancer as well as bone fractures, infection and inflammation.

Gleason Score The Gleason score looks at the pattern of cancer cells within the prostate by examining the biopsy samples. The lower the score, the lower the grade of cancer. Scores are on a range of between 2 to 10. My score of 7 (made up of the 4+3) is moderate, situated between those of slow and more quickly growing tumours. This score is categorised as locally advanced prostate cancer. The first number represents the primary grade of the tumour based on the dominant pattern of the tumour. The second is assigned to the next most frequent pattern. 4+3 is therefore a more advanced cancer than 3+4 although both give a grade of 7.

Antiandrogens Drugs that block testosterone from reaching cancer cells. Most prostate cancers need testosterone to grow.

Bicalutamide Also called Casodex, is an anti-androgen hormone that works by attaching itself to the protein receptors on the surface of the cancer cells. This blocks testosterone from going into the cells and encouraging growth.

Laparoscopic robotically assisted surgery A minimally invasive form of surgery with the instruments and a camera entering the body through several small incisions.

The da Vinci machine A robotic surgical system that allows surgeons to operate with a minimal invasive approach. It is not a robot as it is operated completely by a surgeon using a console. There's a great online video of the da Vinci machine peeling a grape.

Oncology The branch of medicine concerned with the study, classification, and treatment of tumours.

Uro-oncology Urologic oncology deals with genitourinary malignancies such as cancers of the kidney, adrenal glands, prostate, bladder, ureters, testicles or penis.

Urology The branch of medicine concerned with the study and treatment of diseases of the urogenital tract.

MRI scan Magnetic resonance imaging is a type of scan that uses strong magnetic fields and radio waves to produce detailed images of the inside of the body. An MRI scanner is a large tube that contains powerful magnets. You lie inside the tube during the scan.

Ultrasound scan Is a commonly used test that uses sound waves to create images of organs and structures inside your body. As it uses sound waves and not radiation, it is thought to be harmless.

Choline C-11 A chemical tracer injection used in PET scans.

PET scan Positron emission tomography. A radioactive tracer drug is tagged with a natural chemical and put into the patient to provide a 3-dimensional, colour image of the body.

CT scan An X-ray that is often performed on the patient at the same time and in the same machine as the PET scan. It is used to improve the quality of the PET images.

A CT or MRI scan examines the size and shape of body organs and tissue. A PET scan looks at the function of those organs.

TNM A method of measuring how far the cancer has spread. The T stage shows how far the cancer has spread around the prostate. The N stage shows whether the cancer has spread to the lymph nodes and the M stage shows whether cancer has spread to other parts of the body.

Capsule Used to describe the outer membrane of the prostate gland. The prostate does not have a true surrounding capsule but an outer fibromuscular band. It is more accurately called extraprostatic extension (EPE).

SMDT Specialist multi-disciplinary team. Usually made up of a specialist nurse, a urologist (a surgeon who specialises in diseases of the urinary and reproductive systems), an oncologist (a doctor who specialises in cancer treatments other than surgery) and a radiographer (a person who takes X-rays and other scans).

NICE The National Institute for Health and Care Excellence. It provides guidance and advice to improve health and social care. It also had the final say on whether I could have the prostatectomy.

Chapter 2

VTE Deep vein thrombosis stockings are an attractive dark green and come up to the knees.

Djellaba Traditional Berber, long, unisex, outer garment. Looks like a dress.

Urinary leg bag An unattractive rubber bag that can be strapped to the thigh, which serves as a receptacle for urine supplied through a catheter.

Radiotherapy The use of high-energy rays, usually X-rays (such as electrons) to treat disease. It works by targeting and destroying cancer cells in the identified area.

Chemotherapy A treatment that uses anti-cancer (cytotoxic) drugs to destroy cancer cells.

The Radicals Trial A study in which volunteers are randomly placed in one of 2 categories. The first is where radiotherapy is given 3-6 months after the prostatectomy and the second where radiotherapy is given only if the PSA level starts to rise.

Chapter 3

Peyronie's disease Also known as induratio penis plastica and is caused by scar tissue, called plaque, which forms along the length of the penis in the corpora cavernosa which can cause the penis to bend, making sexual intercourse difficult. It is usually caused by damage to the penis.

Nip & Tuck Lue or Nesbit surgical procedures are both used to straighten bent penises. The Lue process involves incision of the plaque and additional vein grafting. The Nesbit procedure is more commonly used and involves an elliptical area of tissue being removed from the healthy (longer) side of the penis to restore symmetry.

Viagra and Cialis Drugs used to treat erectile dysfunction.

The Titan OTR penile implant An inflatable penile prosthesis with a self-contained hydraulic system. The penile cylinders are implanted into the corpora cavernosa of the penis, the pump into the scrotum and the reservoir into the lower abdomen.

Injection A syringe with a fine needle is used to inject a dose of Alprostadil into the penis. Alprostadil is a prostaglandin that works by relaxing certain muscles in the penis and widening blood vessels, which increases blood flow to the penis and helps to cause an erection. It's a bit uncomfortable.

Chapter 4

The immune system A system of biological structures and processes within an organism that protect against disease. When functioning properly it is remarkably effective in identifying and removing pathogens from the body and it is likely that a person with a fully functioning immune system will not get cancer. A deficient immune system cannot properly deal with infections.

Chelation A method of removing certain heavy metals from the bloodstream, used especially in treating lead or mercury poisoning.

DNA adducts Cancer-causing chemicals bonded to a person's DNA

Malondialdehyde (MDA) a naturally occurring product of lipid peroxidation and prostaglandin biosynthesis that is mutagenic and carcinogenic – so there!

Antioxidants Man-made or natural substances that may prevent or delay some types of cell damage often caused by free radicals. They are found in many foods, including fruits, vegetables and some teas.

Cytotoxic Toxic to living cells. Chemotherapy uses cytotoxic drugs designed to kill cancer cells.

Free Radicals Unstable molecules that can damage the cells in your body. They form when atoms or molecules gain or lose electrons. They often occur as a result of normal metabolic processes.

Alkaline diet There are many charts available showing lists of acidic and alkaline foods and they are all different. The best show a range of foods that are tested not by whether the actual food is acidic but whether it remains acidic after metabolism and if it acidifies the body. Some of the results are surprising. E.g. lemons and grapefruits although containing citric acid have an alkalising effect on the body. Cancer is known to favour an acidic environment.

PSMA scan Prostate-specific membrane antigen scans are given to newly diagnosed prostate cancer patients and to those who have had a prostatectomy and have an increasing PSA level. A special molecular body that binds with prostate cancer cells is combined with a radioactive material that can be detected by a gamma camera to form 3- dimensional images of any tumour in the body.

Chapter 5

VMAT A newer way of giving IMRT (Intensity Modulated Radiotherapy). IMRT shapes the beams and allows different doses of radiotherapy to be given. The VMAT (also called Rapid Arc) reshapes the beam as it moves around you. It is more accurate and shortens treatment time.

LINAC Medical linear accelerator. It customises high-energy X-rays or electrons to conform to a tumour's shape and destroy cancer cells while sparing surrounding normal tissue.

Gy Symbol for the gray, the unit of ionising radiation dose. It corresponds to the absorption of one joule of radiation energy per kilogram of matter.

USEFUL ORGANISATIONS

Prostate cancer UK

www.prostatecanceruk.org

An organisation dedicated to stop men dying from prostate cancer. Offers advice and help and publishes a wide range of information booklets.

Macmillan Cancer Support

www.macmillan.org.uk

Practical, financial and emotional support for people with cancer and their families.

Cancer Help UK

www.cancerresearchuk.org

Patient information from Cancer Research UK.

Maggie's Centres

www.maggiescentres.org

A network of drop-in centres around the UK offering free advice and support on cancer. These centres are all beautifully designed by outstanding architects and put emphasis on the environment being an important factor in cancer care.

Philip Weeks Clinic

www.philipweeks.co.uk

Naturopath and nutritional therapist.

Penny Brohn Cancer Care

www.pennybrohncancercare.org

Runs courses and offers physical, emotional and spiritual support to those with cancer and their families.